NUTRiBULLET®
Natural Healing Foods

SUPERCHARGE your HEALTH in just seconds a day!

Table of Contents

Table of Contents

Table of Contents

Where to Find Ingredients

Grocery retailers nationwide are growing more aware of healthy living, and are increasing their stock of organic fruits, vegetables, and superfoods. As a result, many of the ingredients listed in this book can be found at your neighborhood grocery store.

The following ingredients may require a trip to your local specialty health store. Produce marked with an asterisk (*) may be seasonal, and only available at certain times of the year. Check with your grocer to see when these crops are sold.

Ingredients

- Almond Butter
- Apple Cider Vinegar
- Arugula*
- Barley
- Blackstrap Molasses
- Cacao (powder, nibs, or beans)
- Collard Greens*
- Ginger Root*
- Goji Berries
- Kale*
- Papaya*
- Swiss Chard*
- Tahini
- Turmeric
- Turnip Greens

www.nutribullet.com

Put your health in your own hands

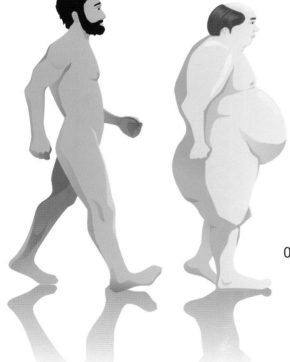

Over the past few decades, America has become the most overfed yet undernourished nation in the World.

When we feel sick, we go straight to the doctor's office, looking for a quick fix to relieve whatever ails us. And we think we are well again.

We get pills for feeling dizzy, pills for feeling sad, pills for high blood pressure, high cholesterol, indigestion, erectile dysfunction – you name it! Yet despite the EVER-INCREASING variety of medicine available, current middle aged Americans report feeling less healthy than the generation that preceded them!*

Our life expectancies are reducing, as are those of our children, who are expected to live 10 years LESS than we are. And most of us are dying from a small handful of the same AVOIDABLE diseases.

*Source: http://www.nih.gov/news/pr/mar2007/nia-05.htm

LEADING CAUSES OF DEATH IN THE U.S.*

1	**Heart Disease**
2	**Cancer**
3	**Chronic Lower Respiratory Diseases**
4	**Stroke**
5	**Accidents**
6	**Alzheimer's Disease**
7	**Diabetes**
8	**Influenza and Pneumonia**
9	**Kidney Diseases**

*Source: http://www.cdc.gov/nchs/fastats/lcod.htm

Why then, with all of the incredible medical advancements of the past 50 years, are we getting less healthy as a population? It is because we are avoiding responsibility for our own health: failing to choose to live a healthy lifestyle, and instead relying on prescription medicines, which often only treat the *symptoms* and not the underlying causes of our health problems.

So how do we reclaim our health?

If we want to regain TRUE health, we must eat and properly digest real, whole foods. Each day, the link between diet and disease becomes more and more apparent. Since processed food entered the Standard American Diet in the mid-twentieth century, hospital visits, medicine prescriptions, and instances of obesity and its related issues have steadily increased. First came margarine, then fast food and frozen dinners, and now most Americans don't understand what real, WHOLE food is. Yes, the term "whole food" had to be created to define food not produced in a factory.

Is your food robbing your health?

Most of the foods sold in a typical market rob us of our health. We MUST steer clear of these unhealthy food products if we want to avoid contributing to gruesome American health statistics. We MUST change the way we eat. We need to SIGNIFICANTLY reduce the amount of processed food included in our diet.

If we don't get back to basics and start eating plenty of fresh fruit, vegetables, whole grains and unaltered meat, our prognosis could be horrible. According to the American Cancer Society, half of all men and one-third of all women in the United States will develop cancer at some point in their lives. The American Heart Association states that over 82 million Americans suffer from some form of heart disease, and over 780,000 of these people die each year. These are tragic statistics considering that these diseases can be prevented and potentially reversed—not with a pill or one doctor's visit, but with a commitment to following healthy eating habits.

The Path to Vibrant Health

The fact that you have purchased the **NUTRIBULLET** system shows that you are ready to take charge of your health. And here is the best news: the **NUTRIBULLET** makes it easier than you ever thought possible to absorb life changing nutrient extracted foods that NOURISH your body on a cellular level. Best of all, it takes no time at all to feel the results. Most start feeling better the very first time they drink a **NUTRIBLAST!**

This book, Natural Healing Foods, gives in-depth descriptions of the systems of the body and profiles specific foods that can prevent and reverse our culture's most preventable diseases. It also provides a wide array of delicious and healthy recipes for **NUTRIBLASTS**— the **NUTRIBULLET's** unique nutrition-packed beverages. It is our goal to educate readers on the amazing inner workings of the body, and advise them how to care for theirs in the best way possible.

For those looking to really KICK START their own personal health reform, Natural Healing Foods includes the **NUTRIBULLET 6 Week Transformation Plan.** This step-by-step plan sets you on the path to optimum health in a FEW SHORT WEEKS! Those who have followed this plan have reported incredible results, including lower blood pressure and cholesterol, reduced symptoms of fibromyalgia, relief from migraines and hot flashes, weight loss, reduced joint pain and increased athletic performance.

So what are you waiting for? Turn the page and start nourishing each major organ system of your body with the BEST foods on earth prepared in the MOST BENEFICIAL way possible!

Nourishing Your Circulatory System

Role of the Circulatory System

The circulatory system is made up of a collection of vessels and organs that distributes life-giving fluids throughout the body. These fluids deliver nutrients to the tissues of your body, giving each cell the energy it needs to survive and thrive. The circulatory system can be divided into two parts: the lymphatic system and the cardiovascular system.

The lymphatic system produces and nourishes blood cells. It also plays a huge role in immune functioning, which will be addressed further in the Immune System portion of this book.

The cardiovascular system refers to the complicated network of veins and arteries that carry heart-pumped blood throughout the body. The heart serves as the hub of this network, and each heartbeat transports blood to nearly every part of your body. The heart supplies our organs with the oxygen, nutrients, and chemicals they need to carry out their unique functions. This intricate system requires constant motion, and because every other organ system in the body depends so heavily on the blood, **any** interruption in the blood pumping process can have dangerous consequences. So let's make sure we feed this system properly!

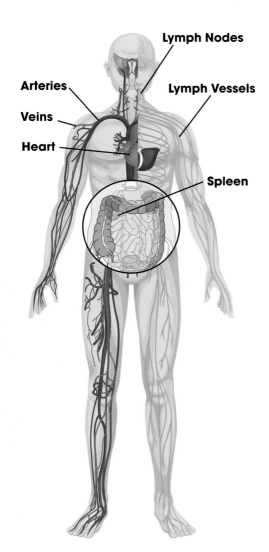

Lymph Nodes

Arteries

Veins

Heart

Lymph Vessels

Spleen

Components of the Circulatory System

The circulatory system can be divided into the lymphatic and cardiovascular systems.

The lymphatic system consists of lymph fluid, lymphatic vessels, the lymph nodes, the tonsils, and the spleen.

The cardiovascular system is made up of the blood, heart, arteries, and veins.

Did you know?

If you lined all of the branches of the average person's blood vessels in a straight line they would total over 60,000 miles? That's two and a half times the circumference of the earth!

Cardiovascular Risk Factors

Cardiovascular disorders are the most widespread health issues in America. From heart disease to blood clots, clogged arteries to irregular palpitations, dangerous heart and blood vessel problems hospitalize and kill millions each year. While some of these problems are present from birth, most result from unhealthy lifestyle choices. Smoking, inactivity, and poor diet are **known** to contribute to a variety of cardiovascular problems.

Smoking raises blood pressure, narrows the blood vessels, and increases the likelihood of developing dangerous blood clots. A lack of exercise fails to raise the heart rate, slowing the rate at which blood circulates throughout the organs. This leads to fatigue, weakened heart muscles, and high blood pressure.

Unhealthy eating habits **pose a huge risk** to cardiovascular health. Eating a diet low in nutrients and high in sugar, salt, cholesterol, and fat, can trigger the buildup of bad cholesterol in our arteries. This cholesterol hardens into plaque that lines the blood vessels, leaving less room for blood to flow through and increasing blood pressure. Arteries can even become completely blocked with plaque—a condition that leads directly to heart attack.

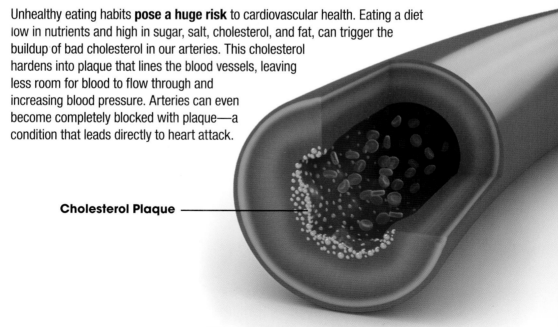

Cholesterol Plaque ⎯⎯⎯⎯⎯⎯⎯

CARDIOVASCULAR FACTS

According to the American Heart Association:

 Over 780,000 people die from heart disease each year in America

 Coronary heart disease causes 1 out of every 6 deaths in the United States

 On average, someone will die from heart disease every 39 seconds, someone will suffer a stroke every 40 seconds

 Over 76 million people, or one in three adults over the age of 20, have high blood pressure

 Heart disease and stroke cost patients over 173 billion dollars annually

-American Heart Association data collected in 2008.

Potential Heart Diseases

Aortic Atherosclerosis
Clogged arteries

Aortic Stenosis
Narrowing of the Aortic Valve—one of the main blood-pumping valves of the heart due to cholesterol or plaque buildup; can lead to congestive heart failure

Cardiomyopathy
Malfunctioning of the heart muscle

Congestive Heart Failure
Inability of the heart to supply the body with sufficient amounts of blood; usually results from one or several other heart problems

Endocarditis
Inflammation of the inner lining of the heart chambers and valves

Heart Attack
Occurs when blood supply to the heart is interrupted; results in death of heart tissue cells

Hypertension
High blood pressure

Hypotension
Low blood pressure

Mitral Valve Prolapse
Collapse of the mitral valve—which regulates blood flow out of the heart

Stroke
Loss of brain functioning that results from a lack of blood flow to the brain

Thrombosis
Blood Clots

Did you know?

The average heart beats 100,000 times each day to pump roughly 2,000 gallons of blood through the body!

Preventing Cardiovascular Problems

While age and genetics factor into a person's risk of developing cardiovascular disease, eating a diet rich in nutrients can **fight** the buildup of harmful plaque and can even reverse existing cardiovascular damage. Abstaining from all tobacco products, getting plenty of exercise, and perhaps most importantly, eating a healthful, nutrient-dense diet can help to prevent future heart troubles and reverse problems like high cholesterol and high blood pressure that can lead to heart attacks, heart failure, and stroke.

The **NUTRIBULLET** is your tool for absorbing all the nourishing, heart-healthy nutrients you need. Just one **NUTRIBLAST** a day can pack more than a day's worth of cholesterol-fighting, plaque-clearing vitamins and minerals to keep your ticker ticking for years to come!

Did you know?

Women's hearts tend to beat faster than men's—a woman averages 78 beats per minute, while a man averages 70 beats per minutes.

Blasting for Cardiovascular Health

Whether looking to maintain good heart health, prevent the onset of heart disease, or reverse troublesome conditions like high cholesterol or high blood pressure. Every heart can benefit from incorporating the following foods into their diet:

1. Berries
Blackberries, blueberries, raspberries, and strawberries are low in calories and high in both soluble fiber (which lowers blood cholesterol levels) and free radical-fighting antioxidants. They are also absolutely delicious! Enjoy!

2. Beans (all types)
Beans are high in soluble fiber, which reduces blood cholesterol levels. Lower cholesterol levels can reduce the risk of developing atherosclerosis!

3. Monounsaturated fats
Found in avocados, flax seeds, chia seeds, nuts and cold water fish like salmon, these good fats (which include omega 3 fatty acids) decrease inflammation, and lower saturated triglyceride levels.

4. Dark leafy greens
Greens like spinach, kale, chard, and arugula are high in fiber and loaded with antioxidants. They are also linked to lower levels of certain enzymes in the body that contribute to heart disease.*

5. Whole grains
Oats, whole wheat, brown rice, quinoa, and other unprocessed grains contain fiber, vitamins, and minerals that greatly reduce the risk of heart-related illness.

Please consult your doctor before beginning this or any other dietary program, especially if you are currently taking any prescription or over-the-counter medication, are pregnant, a minor or any individual with any type of medical condition. The information contained in this guide is designed to maintain good health and does not claim to treat or cure disease. It is not a substitute for regular medical care. Always consult your physician for medical advice and before beginning any dietary program.

Best Blasts for Heart Health

Omega Mix
- 50% Arugula
- 1/2 of one avocado
- 1 plum, pitted
- 1 tbs flax or chia seed
- water: top with water to MAX LINE and extract

I Bran So Far
- 1/4 cup wheat bran, milled in NURIBULLET with milling blade
- 50% collard greens
- 1 banana
- 1/2 cup blueberries or strawberries
- 10 raw almonds
- water: top with water to MAX LINE and extract

Avocacao Ambrosia
- 50% spinach
- 1 cup blueberries
- 1/2 avocado
- 2 tbs raw cacao powder
- water: top with water to MAX LINE and extract

Bean Me Up, Scotty
- 75% romaine
- 2 dates
- 1/3 cup cooked white beans
- water or almond milk: top to MAX LINE and extract

Purple Heart
- 50% Kale
- 1 cup blackberries
- ½ banana
- 1/3 cup cooked black beans
- 10 almonds
- 2 tbs raw cacao
- water: top with water to MAX LINE and extract

C-Side
- 50% kale
- 1 orange
- ½ of one red bell pepper
- 1/2 one avocado
- 10 raw cashews
- 10 walnut halves
- 1/2 tsp pure vanilla extract
- water: top with water to MAX LINE and extract

Popeye and Olive Oyl
- 50% spinach
- 1 apple, sliced into pieces
- 1/4 cup whole rolled oats
- 1 tbs olive oil
- water: top with water to MAX LINE and extract

Sweet Heart
- 50% mixed greens
- 1 frozen banana
- ½ cup frozen raspberries
- 10 hazelnuts
- 2 tbs raw cacao
- 1/2 tsp pure vanilla extract
- water: top with water to MAX LINE and extract

Nourishing Your Immune System

Role of the Immune System

The immune system protects the body from illness, infection, and disease. This complex system uses different body tissues and chemical reactions to defend our bodies from harmful invaders like bacteria, viruses, microbes, free radicals, and parasites. Different types of invaders trigger immune responses and produce antibodies—proteins produced by the immune system to defend the body. Over time, the body builds memory of which antibodies to use for each kind of invader, so protection becomes routine.

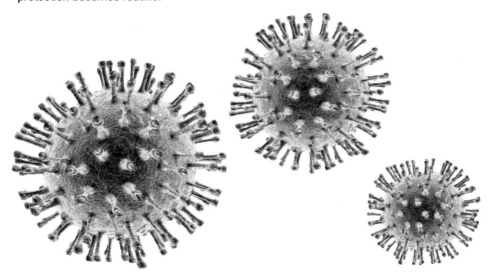

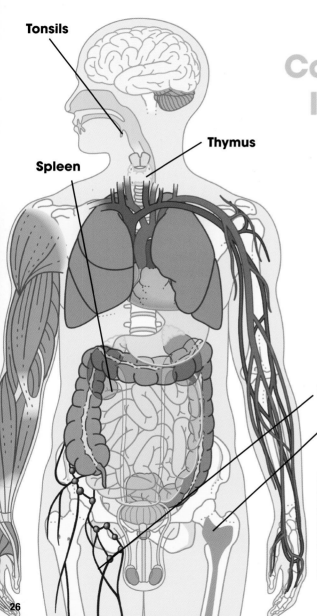

Tonsils

Spleen

Thymus

Components of the Immune System

The **Lymphatic System** plays a large role in immune function. **Lymph Vessels** circulate and drain body fluids known as **lymph** to and from our organs. **Lymph** transports nutrients to the organs and removes any excess substances from them. **Lymph** also contains **white blood cells**—the soldiers of our body that kill a **wide** range of harmful invaders. White blood cells are manufactured in the **thymus** and **bone marrow,** then released into the **lymph** and circulated through the lymph vessels to their final destination.

Lymph Vessels

Bone Marrow

White Army

Your blood contains roughly 50 billion white blood cells with the sole responsibility of maintaining your body's natural defenses. No need to worry if you lose 5 billion when you give blood - you still have a few left.

Risk Factors for the Immune System

Diet and lifestyle play a huge role in our immune system's ability to keep our body functioning at its best. Unhealthy habits significantly increase the number of harmful chemical compounds our body takes in. These compounds, known as **free radicals**, are present in abundance in processed foods and alcohol. Free radicals also enter the body when we breathe in cigarette smoke, paint fumes, exhaust fumes, and other gasses and pollutants in the air.

Free radicals destabilize healthy atoms in the body, causing cell damage that may eventually lead to illness and disease. When our immune system constantly works to defend against free radicals, it has fewer resources available to fight off other invaders like viruses and bacteria, which is why we tend to get sicker when we fail to eat healthfully or live a wholesome lifestyle.

Basically, the more free radicals we take in, the harder it becomes for our immune system to keep us healthy. The fewer free radicals we take in, the more available our immune system is to seek and destroy other harmful invaders.

IMMUNE STATISTICS

THE IMMUNE SYSTEM is closely linked to cancer —the second leading cause of death in the United States
-CDC, 2011

Approximately **1 in 2 MALES and 1 in 3 FEMALES** will contract cancer over the course of their lifetime
-American Cancer Society, 2011

An estimated **23.5 MILLION AMERICANS** suffer from autoimmune disease, and incidences are on the rise
-US Dept. of Health + Human Services, 2010

OVER 40 DISEASES have been classified as having autoimmune roots; these diseases can be both chronic and deadly
-National Institute of Allergy + Infectious Diseases, 2004

Autoimmune diseases collectively rank as a **TOP 10 CAUSE OF DEATH** in women from ages 10-64
-American Journal of Public Health, 2000

Disorders of the Immune System

Because it fights to ward off disease and infections every day, the immune system plays an essential role in protecting our health. It is involved in everything from repairing a paper cut to killing life-threatening parasites. Every illness, injury, and threat to the body requires an immune response in order to heal.

When compromised, however, the immune system may let in bacteria and viruses, which cause conditions like colds and flus. If overworked, protective immune responses may even harm the body—causing issues like chronic inflammation and autoimmune disease, which occur when the immune system attacks healthy body tissues. The development of cancer is also linked to a compromised immune system.

I. Common viral and bacterial infections

The immune system is the body's first line of protection against viruses like the common cold and influenza (flu), as well as bacterial infections like pneumonia, salmonella, urinary tract infection, and ear infection. While some of these conditions can eventually sort themselves out, others can be quite serious and demand medical attention.

We are exposed to germs that cause illness every day. It is so important to keep the immune system strong so it can isolate and attack the bacteria or viruses that enter our system.

II. Inflammation

Inflammation is part of our normal immune response. When the body is harmed, it sends lymph and white blood cells through the lymphatic system to flood the area of concern. This fluid uses chemical reactions to separate and remove the harmful substances, restoring the cells back to their normal state.

While brief periods of inflammation—known as acute inflammation—work to heal the body, inflammation that extends for long periods of time (chronic inflammation) puts a strain on the circulatory and immune systems, damages body tissues, and destroys cells. Chronic inflammation can be attributed to a diet high in processed foods and/or to food sensitivities and allergies. Chronic inflammation makes the body more prone to contracting **other** illnesses and may even cause autoimmune diseases—health problems that occur when the immune system attacks healthy tissues in the body. Autoimmune diseases include Celiac (gluten) Disease, Cirrhosis of the Liver, Crohn's Disease, Lupus, Anemia, Psoriasis, Arthritis, and Type I Diabetes among others.

Eating properly can drastically reduce and reverse chronic inflammation, while eating processed foods can cause its development.

III. Cancer

Cancer occurs when mutated cells reproduce uncontrollably, forming malignant (harmful) tumors that can invade and eventually take over other parts of the body. There are over 100 types of cancer, and the disease can occur in virtually any body part.

The risk of developing cancer depends both on genetics and your surrounding environment. Having a family history of the disease, smoking, being exposed to radiation, and eating a poor diet all increase a person's cancer risk. However, much evidence suggests that eating natural, highly nutritious foods can swing even the most at-risk individuals back to the other side of the spectrum.

Free Radicals and Antioxidants

The theory that links the presence of **free radicals** in the body to an increased cancer risk is gaining support in both medical and holistic healing circles. Free radicals are molecules taken in from the environment that lack an electron. This missing electron makes the free radical molecule unstable and prone to stealing electrons from other surrounding atoms. When ingested, free radicals steal electrons from the atoms of healthy cells. This process has been cited as a cause of premature aging and a host of illnesses and diseases including cancer.

Antioxidants neutralize free radicals. They do this by donating one of their own electrons to the free radical, so the free radical stops looking for an electron to steal. Antioxidants remain stable, even after they give an electron to a free radical. Certain nutrients, like vitamin C and E are particularly good at protecting the body against destructive free radicals. The BEST way to ensure you are getting a sufficient intake of antioxidants is by eating a balanced diet consisting of at least 5-8 servings of fruits and vegetables per day.

Preventing Immune Issues

Living a healthy lifestyle is the KEY to maintaining a powerful immune system. Keep your free radical intake low and your antioxidant intake high by avoiding processed foods and fatty meats, and eating a wide variety of antioxidant-rich fruits, vegetables, nuts, seeds, and lean proteins. Abstain from smoking and recreational drugs, and learn healthy ways to deal with stress, as the body's stress response can weaken the immune system.

The following sections lists specific foods, vitamins, and minerals that can help boost general immunity and reduce inflammation. Extracting nutrient-dense foods in the **NUTRIBULLET** can significantly improve the power of your immune system, protecting your body against toxins, free radicals, and autoimmune disorders, as well as harmful bacterial and viral infections. You are only as healthy and strong as your immune system, so extract your foods, and drink to your health!

Blasting to Boost Immunity

1. Carrots, bell peppers, dark leafy greens

These vegetables contain high levels of vitamin A, a vitamin that protects the body from infection by moistening mucous membranes and producing healing enzymes.

2. Sunflower seeds, almonds

Both foods are high in vitamin E—fat-soluble compounds that serve as **powerful** antioxidants. They also keep skin and hair healthy, and play a large role in the prevention of both bladder and prostate cancers as well as Alzheimer's Disease.

3. Papaya, strawberries, citrus, broccoli

These foods are all high in vitamin C, possibly the most well known immune booster of all the vitamins. Vitamin C stimulates the production of white blood cells—cells that attack invaders in the body. It also plays a role in protecting the joints and eyes, and preventing certain kinds of cancer. Vitamin C is a powerful antioxidant that has been shown to squelch free radical formation.

4. Spelt, sesame seeds, pumpkin seeds, oats

All of these foods contain zinc—an element that maintains white blood cell levels and helps to heal wounds.

5. Garlic

Garlic is known to have antibacterial and antiviral properties, and is also helpful in preventing cancers—especially renal (kidney) and colorectal cancers.

 Getting a proper amount of zinc daily has been shown to improve acne conditions.

Please consult your doctor before beginning this or any other dietary program, especially if you are currently taking any prescription or over-the-counter medication, are pregnant, a minor or any individual with any type of medical condition. The information contained in this guide is designed to maintain good health and does not claim to treat or cure disease. It is not a substitute for regular medical care. Always consult your physician for medical advice and before beginning any dietary program.

Immune Boosting Blasts

A to Zinc

- 50% arugula
- 1 banana
- 1 yellow pepper
- 1 cup of strawberries
- ¼ cup of pumpkin seeds
- water: top with water to MAX LINE and extract

Sick Off You

- 50% collard greens
- 1 orange, peeled
- 10 almonds
- 2 tbs sesame seeds
- water: top with water to MAX LINE and extract

Flu Fighter

- 50% Swiss chard
- 1 carrot, peeled and cut into chunks
- 1 cup strawberries
- 1 tbs sunflower seeds
- 1 tbs pumpkin seeds
- water: top with water to MAX LINE and extract

Citrus System

- 1 orange
- ½ lemon
- ½ lime
- ginger (finger tip)
- sea salt
- 2 TBSP honey
- water: top with water to MAX LINE and extract

Power Punch

- 50% spinach
- 1 banana
- 1 cup papaya
- 1/4 cup rolled oats
- 2 tbs sesame seeds
- water: top with water to MAX LINE and extract

Smooth Season

- 25% Swiss chard
- 25% mustard greens
- 1/2 avocado
- 1 cup papaya
- 1/4 cup rolled oats
- 1 tbs pumpkin seeds
- water: top with water to MAX LINE and extract

First Defense

- 25% spinach
- 25% parsley
- 1/2 orange
- 1 cup strawberries
- 2 tbs sunflower seeds
- 1 tbs sesame seeds
- water: top with water to MAX LINE and extract

Blasting to Reduce Inflammation

1. Spinach, blueberries, cherries
These food contain high levels of flavonoids—compounds known to reduce inflammation. They also contain high antioxidant levels.

2. Avocado, salmon, walnuts
All contain omega-3 fatty acids, which have been shown to disrupt the cell signals that trigger inflammation.

3. Papaya, pineapple
Both fruits belong to the bromeliad family, and as such, contain the enzyme bromelain which has shown to reduce inflammatory responses.

4. Turmeric
Renowned for its anti-inflammatory properties, this spice contains curcumin—a compound known to interfere with chemicals that cause inflammation. It is helpful both when ingested, and when applied topically to skin conditions or injuries.

Laugh Your Troubles Away:
Studies show that people who lack humor in their lives tend to have less protective immune responses.

Anti-Inflammatory Blasts

Flame Thrower
- 50% spinach
- 1/2 avocado
- 1 cup papaya
- 10 walnuts
- water or almond milk: fill to MAX LINE and extract

Cherry on Top
- 50% spinach
- 1 banana
- 1 cup cherries, pits removed
- 10 walnuts
- water or almond milk: fill to MAX LINE and extract

Swell Soother
- 50% spinach
- 1/2 cup blueberries
- 1/2 cup pineapple
- 1 tsp maca powder
- water: top with water to MAX LINE and extract

Deep Purple
- 50% spinach
- 1 banana
- 1/2 cup cherries, pits removed
- 1/2 cup blueberries
- 10 almonds
- water: top with water to MAX LINE and extract

Bromelianaire
- 50% spinach
- 1 cup papaya
- 1/2 cup pineapple
- 2 tbs sunflower seeds
- water: top with water to MAX LINE and extract

Dream Cream
- 50% spinach
- 1/2 avocado
- 1/2 banana
- 10 walnuts
- water: top with water to MAX LINE and extract

NUTRIBULLET SHOW RECIPE!

Turmerific
- 50% spinach
- Piece of pineapple
- Piece of papaya
- ¼ lime
- ¼ lemon
- ¼ grapefruit
- 1 tbsp flax seeds
- ½ tsp turmeric powder
- water: top with water to MAX LINE and extract

Blasting for Cancer Prevention

The vitamins and minerals in the foods we eat act as antioxidants that neutralize free radicals in our system. Antioxidants bond to free radicals, neutralizing them before they can attach to electrons in our cells. Here are several of the top antioxidant foods:

1. **Kale, turnip greens, spinach, broccoli, brussels sprouts, zucchini**
   All are excellent sources of lutein, a carotenoid nutrient known for its powerful antioxidant power. Lutein is fat soluble, so it is best absorbed when eaten with foods high in monounsaturated dietary fats like nuts or avocado. Also, cooking reduces the antioxidant power of lutein; eat these foods as close to their raw natural state as possible.

   Kale, turnip greens, collard greens, and spinach are also high in folate, a B-vitamin linked to the prevention of tumors in the female reproductive system. Low folate intake is also associated with a higher colorectal cancer risk.

2. **Apples, all berries, broccoli, cauliflower, citrus**
   All are excellent sources of flavonoids—powerful antioxidants that may prevent the DNA damage associated with free radicals. Flavonoids also boost absorption of vitamin C, another antioxidant that is particularly important in immune function.

   Blackberries, in particular, have one of the highest flavonoid levels of any food in the world. However, all of these fruits and vegetables are valuable sources of the nutrient.

3. **Green Tea**
   Long celebrated for its antioxidant powers, green tea contains catechin—a powerful flavonoid that has been specifically linked to cancer prevention.

4. Barley, crimini mushrooms, Brazil nuts, brown rice

These foods are all good sources of selenium, a mineral found to significantly reduce the risk of developing lung, prostate, and colorectal cancers.

Top Fresh Antioxidant Foods by volume (per 100g)

1. Blueberries
2. Blackberries
3. Kale
4. Strawberries
5. Spinach
6. Raspberries
7. Brussels Sprouts
8. Plums
9. Broccoli
10. Beets

Cancer Fighting Blasts

Flavor Flavonoid
- 50% kale
- 1 apple
- 1/2 cup blackberries
- 1/2 cup cauliflower
- 2 brazil nuts
- water: top with water to MAX LINE and extract

Tea Time
- 50% spinach
- 1 banana
- 1/2 zucchini
- chilled unsweetened green tea: fill to MAX LINE and extract

Bliss Berry
- 50% turnip greens or kale
- 1/2 avocado
- 1/2 cup blueberries
- 1/2 cup raspberries
- 1/2 cup blackberries
- water or unsweetened green tea: fill to MAX LINE and extract

Apple Blossom
- 50% spinach
- 1 apple
- juice of 1/2 lime
- water or unsweetened green tea: fill to MAX LINE and extract

Rice Rice Baby
- 50% spinach
- 1 banana
- 1/2 orange, peeled
- 1/2 cup cooked brown rice
- 1 brazil nut
- almond milk: fill to MAX LINE and extract

Berryflower
- 50% kale
- 1/2 avocado
- 1 cup mixed berries
- 1 cup cauliflower
- water or chilled unsweetened green tea: fill to MAX LINE and extract

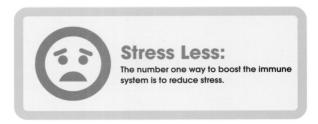

Stress Less:
The number one way to boost the immune system is to reduce stress.

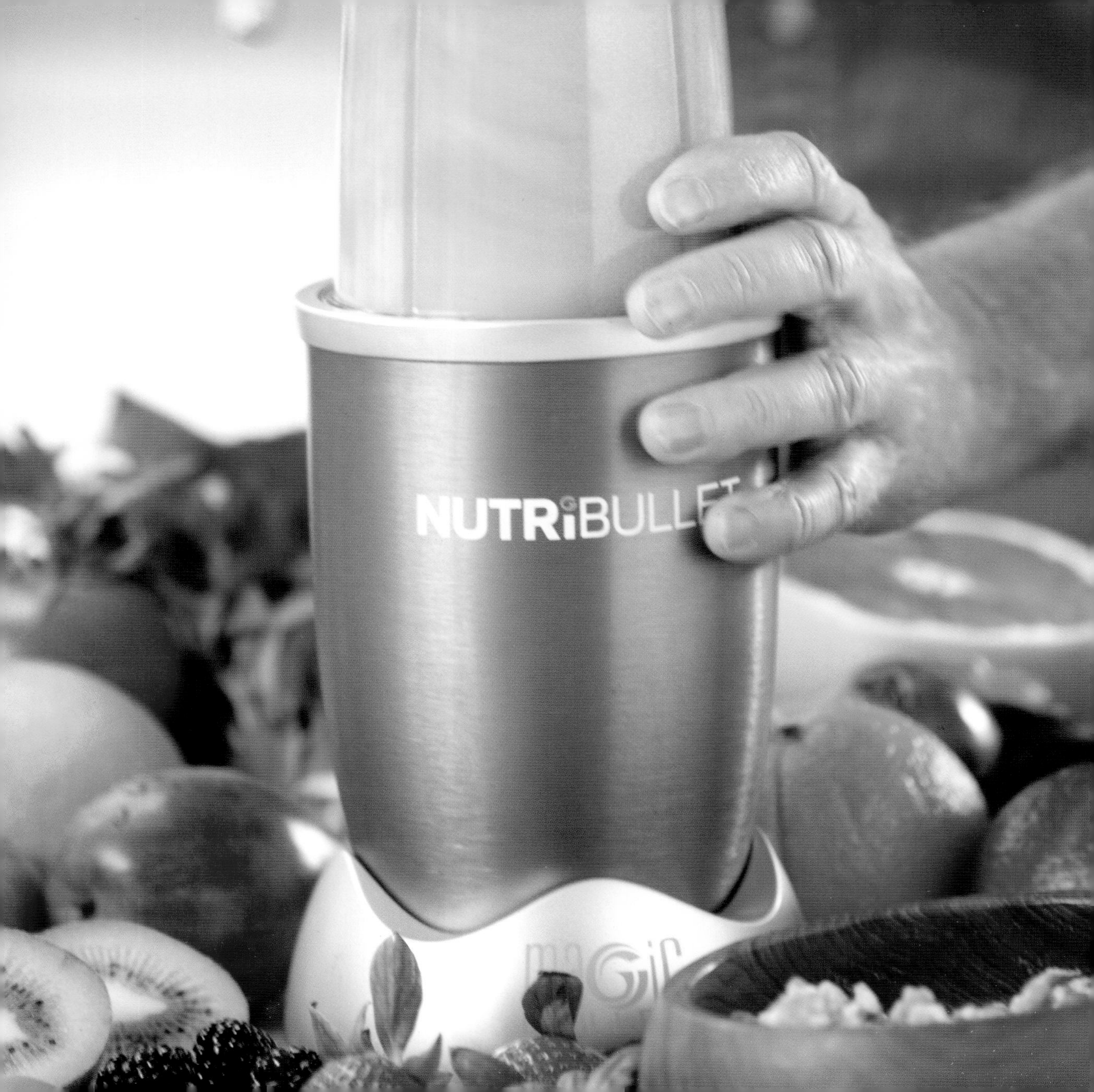
NUTRiBULLET

Nourishing Your Digestive System

Role of the Digestive System

The digestive system allows us to eat, break down, and absorb our food, as well as eliminate food waste. It converts compounds in the foods we eat into the energy that supports all of our other bodily functions.

When fed properly, the digestive system powers us through life, but it is not magic. It can't make quality fuel out of unhealthy ingredients, which is why we must eat healthfully if we want to run at optimum speed.

Digestion itself uses more energy than any other physiological process in the body, making it even more important to consider the nutritional value of everything we eat. Although a cupcake may be delicious, it contains few nutrients and is not worth the effort required of the digestive system to break it down. All of the energy exerted in digesting the cupcake literally gets flushed down the drain, without any benefit to other areas of the body. The better the "fuel" we consume, the better we will operate.

Did you know?
The intestine replaces its lining every 72 hours.

Digestive System

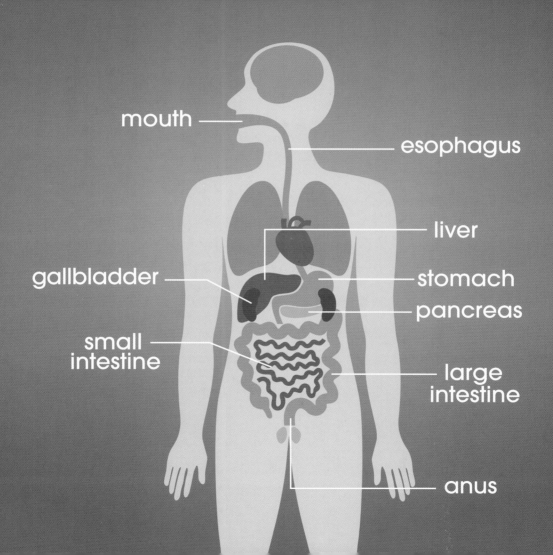

mouth —

esophagus

liver

gallbladder —

stomach

pancreas

small intestine

large intestine

anus

Components of the Digestive System

Made up of the mouth, pharynx, esophagus, stomach, small intestine, large intestine, rectum, anus, and liver, each organ of the digestive system plays a **specific** role to ensure that the body receives enough nutrition.

Digestion begins in the mouth, where we chew food into smaller pieces, break it down with saliva, and swallow it through the pharynx. Once past the pharynx, the swallowed food moves down through the esophagus into the stomach. In the stomach, food mixes with hydrochloric acid that kills potentially harmful germs and starts to break proteins down to be absorbed. This acid-food mixture (known as chyme) then passes through the stomach into the small intestine where food is further digested, and nutrients are absorbed into the bloodstream. Any food particles left unabsorbed move through the small intestine into the large intestine. The large intestine pulls water out of the unabsorbed food, and condenses the remains into solid waste that is removed from the body through the rectum and anus.

Why Nutrient Extracted Food?

Even the healthiest foods require a lot of digestive work in order to be broken down into particles small enough for the body to absorb. This is especially true of fruits and vegetables, which contain tough, rigid fibers that are difficult to digest. Consuming nutrient extracted food is a great choice for anyone in any state of health, because extracted food is virtually predigested—allowing your body to effortlessly absorb and utilize all the nutrition the food has to offer. When we extract foods with the **NutriBullet,** we consume them in their most absorbable state, receiving optimal nutrition without having to rely on chewing, stomach acids, or digestive enzymes to break down our food. It's all done for us!

ROLE OF THE LIVER

- **Produces bile** - liquid that helps break down fats and remove chemicals produced by dead red blood cells from the blood

- **Breaks down nutrients** so they can be absorbed into the bloodstream and transported to the organs

- **Converts all foods into glucose** for energy to be released through the blood stream via insulin

- **Detoxification:** Breaks down harmful chemicals that have entered the body from air, food, cigarettes, alcohol, etc. into smaller, water-soluble compounds to be eliminated through the bile or urine

Though not part of the gastrointestinal tract, the liver plays a large role in delivering the nutrients from food through the blood stream to fuel other organs. The liver also plays a huge role in detoxifying the body, which is explained in further detail in the Detoxification section of this book.

Risk Factors

Because the digestive system processes all of the food that enters your system, what you eat affects its function and efficiency. With digestion, it is equally as important to monitor how you eat as it is to monitor what you eat. Fiber is extremely important in digestive functioning, as it maintains regular elimination, which keeps the colon clean. A lack of fiber in the diet may cause bowels to back up, causing pain and discomfort in the short term, and contributing to the development of more serious disorders like colitis and colon cancer down the line.

It is also important not to overload your system by overeating or swallowing too much air, as both put strain on the digestive tract. Overeating affects digestion at every stage, from contributing to acid reflux in the esophagus, to decreasing nutrient absorption and causing constipation or diarrhea in the intestines. Swallowing too much air can cause painful gas and bloating in the stomach and intestines.

Staying hydrated is also very important in the digestive process, as proper hydration keeps food flowing through the system smoothly.

Like with other organ systems, smoking cigarettes and drinking alcohol can interfere with the digestive process. Both activities increase the chance of developing acid reflux and ulcers, and may keep the body from absorbing key nutrients.

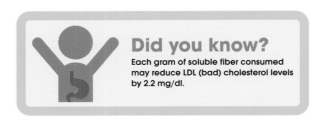

Did you know?

Each gram of soluble fiber consumed may reduce LDL (bad) cholesterol levels by 2.2 mg/dl.

Common Digestive Disorders

The digestive system involves many organs, and issues can develop in any of them. Some, like stomach ache and constipation, can be self-contained problems or symptoms of more serious disorders. Here are several of the most common:

Digestive Disorders

dry mouth
GERD/heartburn (esophagus)
bloating
indigestion
nausea
dyspepsia (stomach ache)
peptic ulcer (stomach)
appendicitis
colitis
celiac disease
constipation
Crohn's disease
diarrhea
diverticulitis
hemorrhoids
Irritable bowel syndrome (small and large intestine)

Prevention of Disorders of the Digestive System

While some digestive issues are caused by disorders in other areas of the body, many can be soothed or healed with proper dietary and eating habits. In general, eating more fiber from low-calorie fruits and vegetables and drinking more water can help food move through the digestive tract efficiently.

Certain foods can also trigger unpleasant digestive reactions, and it is extremely important to pay attention to your body's response to eating. Even healthful foods like tomatoes, whole wheat, nuts, and garlic can cause issues in people with sensitive digestive tracts.

Food intolerances can cause quite a bit of discomfort and can lead to other more serious problems, like chronic inflammation, so please consult with your doctor regarding any specific food issues you may be experiencing.

The **NUTRIBULLET** can significantly improve digestion, because it essentially predigests nutritious foods for you! Extracted food is digested much more efficiently than chewed food, and saves your stomach the stress and strain of dissolving larger pieces of food into their smaller nutritional particles. **NUTRIBLASTS** streamline absorption by the small intestine and elimination from the large intestine, keeping the digestive tract, and the rest of your body in top shape!

Blasting for a Healthy Digestive System

In this section we address common issues that occur in the different areas of the digestive tract.

For Heartburn/GERD:

1. Raw potato, cabbage, or celery
While few people start their day with a tall glass of extracted potato, these fluids can be very helpful in neutralizing stomach acids that cause GERD. If these **NUTRIBLASTS** are too much to take alone, try diluting ¼ cup pure juice with 1 cup of water.

2. Apple cider vinegar
Mix 1 tbs with one cup of water and drink before each meal. There are a few theories on why apple cider vinegar helps acid reflux, but the most accepted thought is that it contracts the sphincter muscle at the base of the esophagus, closing the opening that stomach acids can sneak past.

3. Papaya, pineapple, kiwifruit
These fruits naturally contain the enzyme papain, which is used as an ingredient in many acid reflux medicines.

Did you know?
Digestion requires the use of more energy than any other process in the body.

For Diarrhea:

1. Extracted fruits and vegetables
While fruits and vegetables are the best sources of nutrients, their fiber content may add more stress to an already sensitive digestive system. Extract your plant foods to replenish nutrients lost in diarrhea without overloading your digestive system with foods that are tough to break down.

2. Oregano
The natural oils found in oregano have anti-bacterial, anti-viral, and anti-fungal properties that help kill bacteria or viruses that may cause diarrhea.

3. Yogurt (in small quantities)
Plain yogurt contains helpful strains of bacteria that eat harmful bacteria in the gut. Eat only 4-8 oz of plain yogurt to relieve finicky bowels while avoiding lactose overload. Do not eat yogurt if you are highly lactose intolerant, as this may make diarrhea worse.

For Indigestion:

1. Ginger
Ginger naturally contains painkilling and anti-nausea compounds. If you can handle the spice, it makes an excellent remedy for an upset stomach.

2. Aloe vera juice
Its cooling sensation soothes the stomach. Aloe also has antibacterial, antifungal, and antiviral properties that help kill bacteria or viruses that can cause stomach issues.

3. Brown rice or barley broth
Known to reduce gas and bloating, this mixture is simple to make and highly effective. Boil 1 cup of barley in 5 cups of water for ten minutes, filter the water from the grain, and sip throughout the day.

For Constipation and hemorrhoids:

1. Dark leafy greens, sweet potatoes (skin on), berries, bananas, apricots, dates, figs, oats, wheat bran
These fruits, vegetables and whole grains are high in fiber.

2. Apples, carrots, beets, cabbage, citrus
These fruits, vegetables and whole grains are high in fiber.

3. Coconut water
The electrolytes found within cocunut water are known to hydrate better and faster than regular water. Dehydration is a leading cause of constipation.

Heartburn Healer Blasts

Soothe Operator
- -50% butter lettuce
- -2 stalks celery, diced
- -½ banana
- -1 cup papaya
- -water: top with water to MAX LINE and extract

Off the GERD
- -50% kale
- -1 cup shredded cabbage
- -1 cup pineapple
- -½ avocado
- -1 tbs sunflower seeds
- -water: top with water to MAX LINE and extract

Easy Cider
- -50% spinach
- -1 banana
- -1 kiwifruit, peeled
- -2 tbs apple cider vinegar
- -water: top with water to MAX LINE and extract

Tater Tamer
- -50% butter lettuce
- -1 small raw new potato, cut into quarters
- -1/2 cup pineapple
- -1 kiwifruit, peeled
- -water or coconut water: top with water or coconut water to MAX LINE and extract

Indigestion Correction

Ginger Snap
- -50% butter lettuce
- -1/2 banana
- -1 ripe pear (skin on)
- - ½ inch slice of peeled ginger root
- -1 tsp cinnamon
- -1/2 tsp nutmeg
- -water or almond milk: top with water or almond milk
  to MAX LINE and extract

Aloe-ha
- -50% spinach
- -1 cucumber, peeled
- -1 kiwi, peeled
- -1 cup watermelon
- -gel from one 2" chunk of aloe leaf
- -water or almond milk: top with water or almond milk
  to MAX LINE and extract

Barley Belly
- -50% mixed greens
- -small handful of fresh oregano
- -1 banana
- -1/2 slice peeled ginger root
- -1 cup of chilled barley broth
- -almond milk: top with almond milk to MAX LINE and extract

Constipation Relief

Like Clockwork Orange
- 50% romaine lettuce
- ½ steamed sweet potato (skin included)
- ½ orange, peeled
- 2 medjool dates
- 10 walnut halves
- 2 teaspoons of cinnamon
- water: top with water to MAX LINE and extract

Regularity Refreshment
- 25% kale
- 25% swiss chard
- ½ beet
- ½ apple
- ½ lemon, peeled
- 1 cup of coconut water
- water: top with water to MAX LINE and extract

Clean Sweep
- 50% spinach
- 1 cup shredded cabbage
- 1 carrot, quartered
- 1 banana
- ¼ cup blueberries
- 2 tbs flax or chia seed
- water: top with water to MAX LINE and extract

Movin' and Groovin'
- 50% Swiss chard
- 1/2 steamed sweet potato
- 1/2 cup blueberries
- 2 dried apricots
- coconut water: top with coconut water to MAX LINE and extract

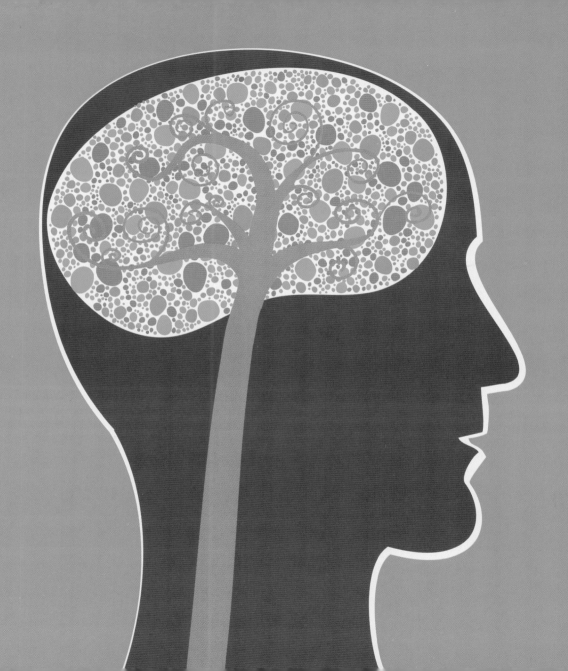

Nourishing Your Nervous System

Role of Nervous System

The Central Nervous System is the body's communication and control center. It controls ALL mental activity including thought, memory and learning. Using receptors, the nervous system detects both external (temperature, light, sound) and internal (blood pressure, pH, glucose levels) input. Your brain makes decisions every second based on all of this input. Your central nervous system has the **huge responsibility** of sending the appropriate signal to the appropriate muscle or gland to produce the proper response to the data received. It is the nervous system that sends signals telling you to jump **away** from a moving car instead of in front of one.

This complicated organ system needs to be well fed! Eating too much or too little of a certain nutrient can have a **huge** impact on brain chemistry. The chemicals that transfer signals between the cells of the nervous system can either stimulate or calm the brain. This has a significant effect on digestion, focus, sleep and mood. Because what we eat **plays such a large role** in dampening or improving mood, we've list some mood balancing foods in this chapter.

Additionally, this section includes foods that support vision, as the retina—the part of the eye that transmits all of the visual input we take in to the brain is also greatly affected by what we eat.

Common Neurological Disorders

Meningitis · ADHD · Multiple Sclerosis · BELL'S PALSY · BRAIN · EPILEPSY · STROKE · TUMOR · ADD · DEMENTIA/ALZHEIMER'S · Migraine · PARKINSON'S DISEASE · CEREBRAL PALSY

Nervous System Disorders

With a system as complicated as the nervous system, one small problem can spell major consequences for the brain and the rest of the body. There are several factors that can lead to neurological disorders including genetics, trauma, and cell decay that naturally occurs with aging. While some of these factors cannot be avoided, others can be delayed and even prevented with a highly nutritious diet. In this section we focus on using nutrition to maintain overall brain health.

Stroke is the #1 cause of neurological damage

One of the leading causes of death nationwide, strokes occur when the brain does not receive enough blood. This results in a swift and possibly permanent loss of brain function. Strokes can develop when blood vessels leading to the brain become blocked, or when blood vessels within the brain rupture. Clogged arteries, blood clots, or head trauma can be responsible for this interruption of normal blood flow. Suffering from a stroke may lead to hearing loss, paralysis, loss of speaking ability, or death, if not treated immediately.

Though strokes occur in the brain, they are also a disorder of the circulatory system. Individuals can reduce their risk of a stroke by following the diet, exercise, and lifestyle highlighted in the **Circulatory System** portion of the book.

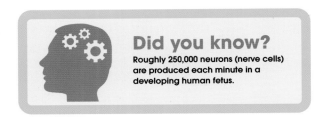

Did you know?
Roughly 250,000 neurons (nerve cells) are produced each minute in a developing human fetus.

Dementia is the #2 cause of neurological damage

Dementia is the term used to describe a gradual decline in healthy brain functioning. **Alzheimer's disease** is the most common form of dementia. Medical experts are still trying to pinpoint exactly what causes **Alzheimer's (**and dementia in general), but they have observed that tangled neurons and plaque buildup in brain tissues generally accompany the condition. These defects may cause some of the problems associated with the disorder.

Alzheimer's disease tends to run in families but may also result from gradually hardening arteries that limit blood flow to the brain over time. Symptoms become worse as a sufferer ages, and he or she may grow more confused, disoriented, restless and unable to carry out normal human functions as time goes by.

Nervous System Disorder Risk Factors

A family history of stroke, mental illness, or vision problems can increase a person's risk of developing similar health issues. However, this can be delayed, prevented and/or possibly reversed with proper nutrition.

Strokes are often caused by cardiovascular problems. A healthy diet free of artery-clogging trans fats, processed foods, and LDL (bad) cholesterol can reduce the cardiovascular issues that can lead to stroke. Also, it is important to avoid smoking. Smoking damages the lining of the blood vessels and increases the likelihood of developing blood clots.

Dementia, Alzheimer's and other degenerative brain disorders are also associated with a high-risk lifestyle. Like with stroke, smoking, drug use, and a low-nutrient, high fat diet can increase the risk of developing Alzheimer's.

Poor diet also plays a **huge** role in depression and other mood disorders, as mood-lifting neurotransmitters ("happy chemicals") in your brain can **only** be made from specific food-based proteins. Diets that do not include these foods restrict the brain's ability to make and release these certain chemicals, leaving us open to developing a mood disorder.

Finally, vision and degenerative eye disorders are often tied to conditions like high blood pressure and diabetes. Both of these conditions relate to diet and lifestyle choices and are often brought on by eating processed foods and foods that are high in sugar.

Nutrition Facts

Serving Size 1 cup (240mL)
Servings Per Container about 4
Calories 110
Fat Calories 20

Amount / serving

Total Fat 2.5g
Saturated Fat 1
Trans Fat 0g
Cholesterol 15mg
Sodium 130mg

Percent Daily Values (DV) are based on a 2,000 calorie diet

Vitamin A 10% • Vitamin C 4
Iron 0% • Vitamin D

ENTS: GRADE A LOWFAT MILK, VITAMIN A PALMITATE,

Nourishing Your Nervous System

Prevention

Like with almost all potential health problems, these nervous system disorders can be delayed, prevented and even reversed by eating a nutrient-rich diet. There are even certain foods, which come next in this section, that have been shown to **specifically** help maintain healthy brain tissue.

The best part is that the **NUTRIBULLET** makes it fast, easy and delicious to ENJOY the brain-healthy foods listed in the next few pages. With just one **NUTRIBLAST** a day you can pack a TON of "brain food" into just one great tasting beverage, PLUS because your **NUTRIBLAST** is so easy for your body to digest, you KNOW you are getting the most out of your food.

Drinking one **NUTRIBLAST** a day can supply your body with the enzymes it needs to produce its feel-good chemicals. You'll be amazed at how extracting nutrient rich fruits, vegetables, nuts and seeds in the **NUTRIBULLET** can help shift your attitude and improve your outlook on life!

BLASTING for Overall Brain Health

The following foods have been shown to support optimum brain function, which can make you sharper, faster, and more functional in everyday life. Researchers are also beginning to discover a strong connection between nutrition, absorption, and the onset of Alzheimer's disease and other forms of dementia in aging patients. So get the following foods in your daily **NUTRIBLAST** and feed that nervous system with the easily absorbed nutrition it needs to keep running in shipshape fashion at ANY age!

1. **Potatoes, Sunflower Seeds (B6); Lentils, Spinach, Collard Greens, Turnip Greens (B9); nonfat plain Greek Yogurt (B12)**
   These foods are particularly high in B-vitamins, which have been observed to slow the rate of brain shrinkage and the onset of Alzheimer's disease in elderly patients.

2. **Sweet potato, Carrots, apricot, cantaloupe (vitamin A); Kale, Swiss Chard (vitamin A& E); Almonds, Papaya, Sunflower Seeds (vitamin E)**
   These foods are rich sources of vitamins A and E, which act as powerful antioxidants throughout the body, and have been shown to specifically prevent the accumulation of free radicals in the brain. Vitamin E may also protect the brain against the invasion of toxic proteins that contribute to the development of Alzheimer's.

3. **Flax Seeds, Walnuts, Avocados**
   These 3 super foods are fantastic sources of ALA omega-3 fatty acids. Widely accepted to improve cardiovascular health, omega 3's are frequently cited to improve overall brain health and delay the onset of neurological aging.

Did you know?
There are more nerve cells in the brain than there are stars in the Milky Way.

Best Brain Blasts

Mind Feeder
-50% spinach
-1/2 avocado
-2 apricots
-10 almonds
-1 tbs sunflower seeds
-water: top with water to MAX LINE and extract

Brain Food
-25% collard greens
-25% Swiss Chard
-1 cup papaya
-1/4 cup walnuts
-2 tbs flax seeds
-water: top with water to MAX LINE and extract

Sweet Memory
-50% turnip or collard greens
-1 banana
-1/2 cup sprouted lentils
-1/2 cup cantaloupe
-1 tbs sunflower seeds
-1 tbs flax seed
-water: top with water to MAX LINE and extract

The Think Drink
-25% kale
-25% spinach
-1/2 one steamed sweet potato
-10 almonds
-2 tbs chia or flax seed
-water: top with water to MAX LINE and extract

Endocrine System

Role of the Endocrine System

The endocrine system is responsible for releasing all of the hormones in your body. Hormones are substances sent throughout the bloodstream that trigger chemical reactions in our cells. These chemical reactions change our body from the inside out, and play a key role in maintaining cell growth, the stress response, sleep cycles, arousal, energy levels, reproductive changes, and homeostasis (which maintains the internal stability of everything from body temperature to "normal weight").

Endocrine Disorders

Addison's Disease: inhibited production of steroids; causes weakness and abdominal pain, low blood pressure, and potentially coma and death in severe cases

Conn's Syndrome: over-production of adrenal gland hormone; can result in high blood pressure and other harmful effects

Cushing's Syndrome: over production of cortisol; may result in rapid weight gain, moon face, high blood pressure, necrosis (skin cell death), and mood swings among other symptoms. Often results from a tumor in the adrenal gland

Diabetes: (page 78)

Thyroiditis: inflammation of the thyroid gland; may result in weight gain, depression, brain fog, dry skin, constipation

Pituitary tumors: result in vision problems, headaches, emotional instability, depression, anxiety, apathy, and irritability

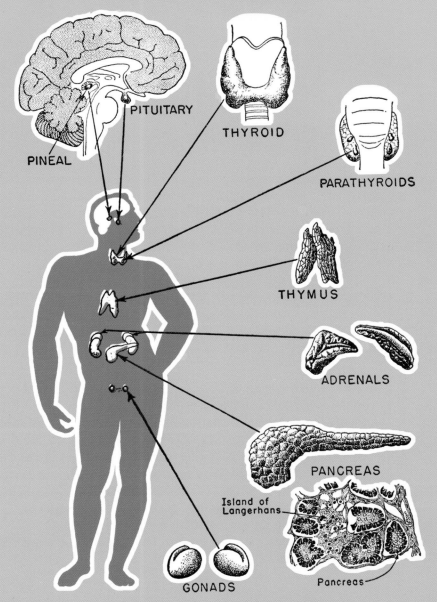

Fig. 104. The endocrine glands.

Components of the Endocrine System

The endocrine system is made up of a collection of glands. These include the hypothalamus, pituitary, thyroid and adrenal glands, as well as the pancreas. Several tissues of other organ systems also contain hormone-secreting glands and function as part of the endocrine system. These include the stomach, liver, heart, bone marrow, adipose (fat) tissue, testicles, ovaries and skin.

Risk Factors for Endocrine System

The effects of hormone disruption in the body range from inconvenient to deadly. While hormonal shifts can result from birth or genetic defects, others can be brought on by age, stress, injury, infection, or illness.

Because different hormones serve different purposes in the body, any overproduction, underproduction, or shift in the balance of hormone levels can interfere with normal physical function. Issues in the endocrine glands are often responsible for hormonal imbalances, and because hormones work along with other body systems, endocrine disorders often surface in other organs. On the other hand, hormonal problems can also be a symptom of non-endocrine diseases.

Diabetes is the most widespread endocrine disorder, and is described in detail on page 78.

Did you know?
The body manufactures over 30 different types of hormones.

Blood Sugar and Diabetes

The pancreas regulates blood sugar levels to fuel your body's metabolism. When the small intestine absorbs food, it quickly releases sugars from the food known as glucose into the bloodstream. The pancreas senses this spike in blood sugar and releases a hormone called insulin that links with glucose molecules and delivers them to cells at a slow and steady rate. This slow and steady delivery of glucose to cells keeps the cells working consistently, and as a result, maintains the body's energy levels throughout the day.

Insulin responses can become strained without a steady and moderate supply of glucose, and eating too much or too little can cause problems for the body's conversion of glucose to energy. When we overeat, we overload our bloodstream with glucose. This puts the body in a state of hyperglycemia (high blood sugar), and the pancreas must strain itself to produce extra insulin to take care of it.

When we do not eat enough throughout the day, our blood sugar levels get very low. The body becomes hypoglycemic (in a state of low blood sugar) and insulin production slows down. Then, once we finally eat, glucose floods an unprepared bloodstream, leaving the pancreas scrambling to produce enough insulin to handle the sudden change in blood sugar.

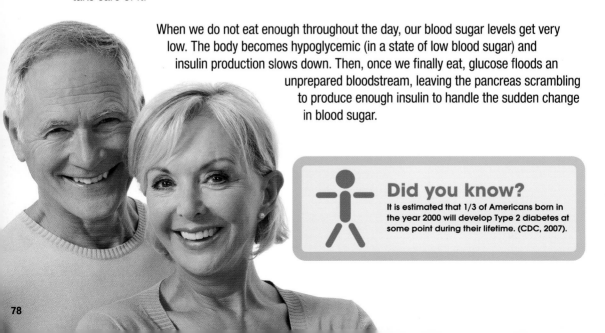

Did you know?

It is estimated that 1/3 of Americans born in the year 2000 will develop Type 2 diabetes at some point during their lifetime. (CDC, 2007).

Constant strain on the pancreas over time can lead to the development of Type 2 Diabetes, which occurs when the insulin response cannot properly manage the amount of glucose present in the blood. While Type 1 Diabetes is most often inherited genetically or prompted by illness, Type 2 Diabetes usually results from years of poor eating habits. Type 2 Diabetes is far more common than Type 1, and accounts for up to 95% of all diabetes diagnoses. The good news is that Type 2 Diabetes can be avoided or reversed with proper eating and lifestyle habits.

Symptoms

Hyperglycemic symptoms: fatigue; thirst; excessive urination/bladder pressure; constant hunger; rapid, unintentional weight loss, vision problems

Hypoglycemic symptoms: hunger, sweating, dizziness, confusion, irregular heartbeat, numbness and/or tingling of the lips

Diabetics can experience symptoms of both hyper and hypoglycemia. You are more at risk for diabetes if you: are overweight or obese, have high blood pressure, have high LDL ("bad") cholesterol, have family history of Diabetes or Heart Disease, or are of African-American, Asian-American, Latin American, Pacific Islander, or Native American descent.

Problems associated with Diabetes include blindness, heart disease, stroke, kidney failure, and poor circulation to the limbs (that may result in amputations).

Blasting for Diabetes

The key to a healthy blood sugar level is consistency and moderation: making sure the blood sugar levels never get too high or too low, so insulin is released at a steady rate.

The efficiency of insulin regulation is directly related to what and how we eat, and the **NUTRIBUL-LET** is an excellent tool to support healthy blood sugar levels. Consuming high fiber, low sugar, and nutrient-dense plant foods on a steady, sensible schedule can significantly improve how your body controls its energy levels. Consuming these foods in a **NUTRIBLAST** adds the digestive efficiency of nutrient extraction, ensuring your body gets exactly what it needs, exactly when it needs it!

1. **High fiber fruits, vegetables, and legumes like leafy greens, berries, cabbage, brussels sprouts, asparagus, apples, and beans**
   Once in the intestines, soluble fiber turns into a gel that slows the absorption of sugars in the blood. This steadies the rate at which the pancreas releases insulin. Insoluble fiber helps blood sugar levels by bulking up foods without adding extra fat, sugar, protein, or calories. This allows the body to feel full on foods that do not release too much glucose, limiting insulin-spikes that can lead to Type 2 Diabetes.

   These plant foods are also high in vitamins and other antioxidants that help combat free radicals especially dangerous to those with Diabetes.

2. **Cinnamon**
   Research suggests that enjoying 1 to 2 teaspoons of cinnamon a day can help the body process insulin.

3. **Swiss chard, sea vegetables, pumpkin seeds, blackstrap molasses**
   These foods carry high levels of magnesium, a mineral that diabetics tend to lack. Magnesium is known to help control glucose levels and prevent damage to the retinae, a common concern among diabetics.

4. **Complex carbohydrates like whole oats, brown rice, quinoa, and whole wheat**
   Complex carbohydrates take time to be converted into glucose in the body, causing a slower, steadier release of insulin than simpler, refined carbohydrates—which spike your blood sugar levels.

5. **Apple, broccoli, corn, grapefruit, sweet potato, tomato**
   A serving of each supplies roughly the daily requirement of chromium, a mineral that helps cells, decreasing the buildup of excess blood sugar.

Insulin Regulating Blasts

Blood Sugar Baby
- -50% Swiss Chard
- -1/2 apple
- -1/2 banana
- -1/4 cup pumpkin seeds
- -10 walnuts
- -2 tsp cinnamon
- -water: top with water to MAX LINE and extract

Nice and Slow
- -50% spinach
- -1/2 avocado
- -1 cup blackberries
- -1/4 cup rolled oats
- -2 tsp cinnamon
- -water: top with water to MAX LINE and extract

Sweet Release
- -50% Swiss Chard
- -1/2 steamed sweet potato
- -2 tbs pumpkin seeds
- -1 tbs coconut oil
- -1 tsp cinnamon
- -water or unsweetened almond milk: top with water or unsweetened almond milk
  to MAX LINE and extract

Broccoli Bunch
- -50% kale
- -1/2 banana
- -1/2 cup blueberries
- -1 cup broccoli
- -12 almonds
- -1 tsp cinnamon
- -water: top with water to MAX LINE and extract

Hormone Imbalance

Both men and women experience changes in sex hormone levels throughout their lives, and an imbalance of these hormones can have negative consequences on the body. From mood swings to increased cancer risks, here are a few issues that hormonal imbalance can cause in both men and women:

Did you know?

The average menstrual cycle lasts 28 days, but a woman's cycle can span anywhere from 23 to 35 days.

In women

PMS

Premenstrual syndrome is believed to result from hormonal changes that occur around one week before menstruation. Estrogen and progesterone levels rise and fall at specific times during the menstrual cycle. Generally, estrogen levels rise, peak and fall during the first two weeks of a woman's cycle, and progesterone does the same during the last two weeks. These peaks and dips of hormonal activity affect signals in the brain and can cause moodiness, irritability, food cravings, anxiety, and insomnia among other symptoms. These symptoms should be minor, and any extremes may reflect an abnormal hormone balance.

Infertility

While there are many factors involved in a woman's ability to have a child, hormonal imbalance is a common cause of infertility. Irregular hormone patterns can interfere with menstrual regularity, which can change a woman's ability to conceive. Additionally, low progesterone levels during pregnancy can lead to miscarriage.

Menopause

Menopause is a natural reproductive progression that marks the end of a woman's fertile years. The ovaries slow their production of estrogen, progesterone, and testosterone as they age, which limits a woman's ability to conceive a child. Menopause occurs when the ovaries stop producing hormones altogether, putting an end to the menstrual cycle.

While estrogen, progesterone, and testosterone have a direct effect on the reproductive organs, they also affect other regions of the body, including the brain, skin, digestive system, and immune system. When a woman's production of these hormones slows and/or halts, she may suffer mood swings, depression, hot flashes, fatigue, poor circulation, bone loss, or weight gain, among other symptoms. With the proper diet, these symptoms can be minimized or even eliminated.

In men

Performance Issues

Men can experience a wide variety of symptoms as a result of hormonal imbalance. Testosterone levels in men tend to drop due to aging and environmental factors, and as a result, men can experience lowered sex drive, erectile dysfunction, and/or lowered sperm count. Additionally, low testosterone levels can bring about fatigue, hair loss, anxiety and/or depression, lowered motivation, and weight gain.

Enlarged Prostate

The prostate gland produces 30% of all seminal fluid. An enlarged prostate gland can block the flow of urine and sperm, and is linked to an increased risk of developing prostate cancer, the second leading cause of cancer death in men.

The prostate gland may enlarge when the body manufactures too much estrogen or DHT—the hormone responsible for prostate growth during puberty. While men do not naturally release enough estrogen to cause issues, a diet of processed snack foods, hormonally injected meat and dairy products, and genetically modified produce has been shown to increase estrogen production in both women and men, which can be dangerous for both sexes.

Did you know?
The average prostate gland is roughly the size of a golf ball.

Endocrine System

Blasting for Reproductive Hormone Regulation

The **NUTRIBULLET** is the ideal tool for feeding your endocrine and reproductive systems the nutrients they need to function properly. Drinking **NUTRIBLASTS** full of nutrient extracted plant foods ensures that your body absorbs all of the enzymes needed to set off the hormone manufacturing process. With healthy hormone functioning, your body, outlook, and life will be more balanced!

Best Foods FOR WOMEN

1. **Swiss Chard and spinach, pumpkin seeds, cashews and almonds**
   These foods all contain high levels of magnesium, which can boost dopamine production in the brain and help the body process estrogen. Women experiencing premenstrual or menopausal mood swings are often magnesium deficient, so eating a diet rich in these foods helps balance moods and relieve cramps and bloating.

2. **Non-rBGH/rBST* plain Greek yogurt, tahini (Sesame seed paste), spinach**
   All of these foods are high in calcium, which has been shown to prevent PMS symptoms and reduce the risk of developing osteoporosis in menopausal women. The dips in estrogen that occur with menopause drain calcium reserves in the body, so it is very important that menopausal women take in enough of this mineral to avoid bone problems.

Blasts for Women

 Female Hormone Balancer
-1/4 small beet
-10 red seedless grapes
-2 sm broccoli florets
-10 raspberries
-1 tbsp goji berries
-½ sm avocado
-1 tsp olive oil
-water: top with water to MAX LINE and extract

Girl's Best Friend
-50% Swiss Chard
-1 banana
-1 tablespoon tahini
-6 almonds
-6 cashews
-water: top with water to MAX LINE and extract

Lady Elixir
-50% spinach
-1 banana
-1/4 cup pumpkin seeds
-12 almonds
-almond milk: top with almond milk to MAX LINE and extract

Cream of the Crop
-25% Swiss chard
-25% spinach
-1/2 avocado
-1/2 banana
-1/2 cup blueberries
-almond milk: top with almond milk to MAX LINE and extract

Best Foods FOR MEN:

1. Tomatoes, watermelon, and grapefruit

These fruits contain large quantities of lycopene—an antioxidant known to protect against prostate cancer

2. Pumpkin seeds, spinach, sunflower seeds

These all contain high levels of zinc, a mineral known to boost immunity, especially in the prostate region. Zinc is also known to raise testosterone levels in men, which improves the sex drive.

3. Hazelnuts, dark leafy greens (kale, chard, spinach), sweet potatoes

All contain large amounts of various B-vitamins, which are known to boost testosterone levels.

Blasts for Men

Male Hormone Balancer
-1/4 small beet
-10 red seedless grapes
-2 sm broccoli florets
-15 blueberries
-1/4 cup of pumpkin seeds
-1 to 2 tbsp olive oil
-water: top with water to
   MAX LINE and extract

Dude Defender
-50% spinach
-1 cup watermelon, seeded
-1/2 grapefruit
-water: top with water to
   MAX LINE and extract

Man Meal
-25% kale
-25% spinach
-1 banana
-1/4 cup hazelnuts
-1/4 cup pumpkin seeds
-water: top with water to MAX LINE and extract

Sunflower Power
-50% kale
-1/2 steamed sweet potato
-1/4 cup sunflower seeds
-water or almond milk: top with water or almond milk to MAX LINE and extract

Did you know?
Alcohol consumption, drug use, and cigarette smoking can warp the shape of sperm or slow their movements, resulting in a lowered chance of conception during intercourse.

Endocrine System

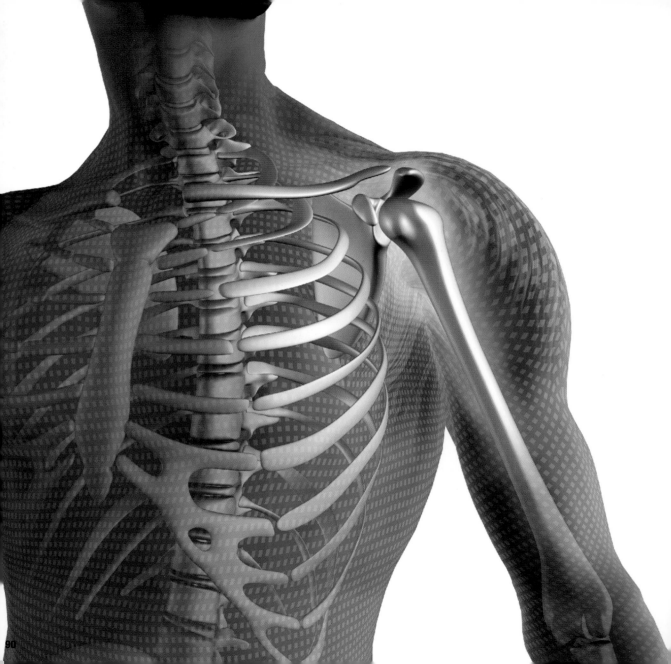

Nourishing Your Skeletal System

Role of the Skeletal System

Made up of the cartilage and roughly 206 bones throughout the body, the skeletal system supports, moves, and protects the body. It also stores vital nutrients (most notably, calcium) within its structures, and regulates blood cell production and certain endocrine functions.

Components of the Skeletal System

The skeletal system is made up of the axial skeleton and the appendicular skeleton. The axial skeleton consists of the spine, ribcage, and skull, and is responsible for keeping the body upright and protecting vital organs like the heart, lungs, pharynx, larynx, throat and brain. The appendicular skeleton, consisting of the pelvis and upper and lower limbs, moves the body through space and protects the reproductive and lower digestive organs.

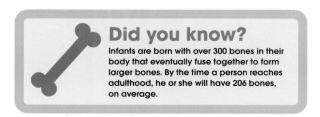

Did you know?

Infants are born with over 300 bones in their body that eventually fuse together to form larger bones. By the time a person reaches adulthood, he or she will have 206 bones, on average.

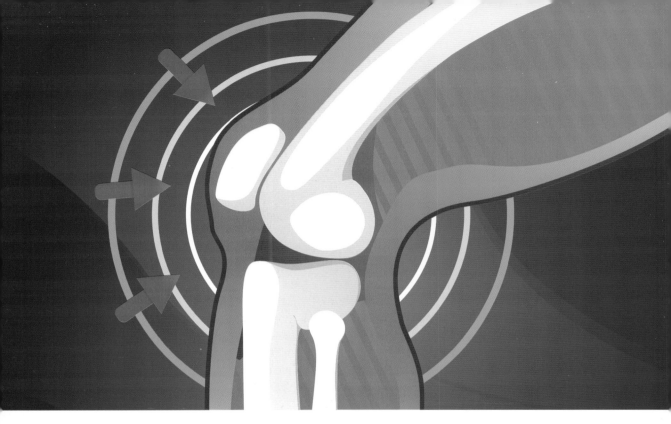

Bones

Despite their solid appearance, bones are actually made up of two different tissues: compact bone and spongy bone. Compact bone forms the outer layer of the bones. It provides structure to the skeleton and protects of the inner core of the bone. Though hard and dense, compact bone contains small pores that surround the nerves of the peripheral nervous system.

Spongy bone contains large pores that house the blood vessels and bone marrow—bone tissue that manufactures red and white blood cells as well as platelets—in certain bones. Marrow can also be found in the interior cavities of various types of bones.

Bone Growth/Destruction

Bones store calcium in their walls. While calcium is structurally important to the skeletal system, other organs also need calcium to carry out their functions. To make sure that other organ systems receive sufficient amounts of calcium, bone cells called osteoclasts break down bone tissue to release calcium molecules into the bloodstream, where they are carried to their final destination. At the same time, different bone cells called osteoblasts rebuild the structures broken down by the osteoclasts and replenish the bone's calcium reserves.

For the first 30 or so years of a person's life, osteoblasts build more bone than osteoclasts break down, resulting in a steady increase in bone mass and density. After age 30, however, osteoblast functioning levels off, slows, and eventually stops, while osteoclasts continue to break bones down. This results in a loss of bone mass and density as we age, and makes it extremely important to receive proper amounts of calcium and exercise up to age 30, and even more important to take in a sufficient amount of calcium after 30, so your body doesn't break down your bones to access the calcium it needs.

Cartilage

Cartilage lines the joints between bones and provides structure to other body parts like the nose, ears, and trachea. It is a firm but flexible material that does not contain blood vessels. It reduces the friction between bones at the joint, and absorbs the shock of movement. Cartilage also protects delicate bones that would otherwise be vulnerable to injury or breakage.

Risk Factors for the Skeletal System

Exercise is extremely important for maintaining bone health. Those who lead inactive lifestyles tend to have lower bone densities than those who exercise regularly.

Nutrition plays an extremely important role in bone health as well—especially the intake of calcium and vitamin D. Eating a diet low in either nutrient greatly increases a person's risk of bone fractures and bone disease. This is especially true of women, who statistically have lower bone densities than men. Additionally, drinking carbonated or caffeinated beverages can wreak havoc on the skeletal system, as both substances have been found to leach calcium from bones and expel it through the urine.

Finally, smoking and drinking alcohol interfere with healthy bone functioning. Smoking interrupts the vitamin D/calcium absorption process, while alcohol alters the hormones responsible for calcium distribution.

Did you know?
There are over 230 moveable and semi-moveable joints in the body.

Osteoporosis

Osteoporosis, which translates into "porous bone" is a disorder in which bone structures deteriorate, leaving the skeleton weak and prone to fractures. Listed below is a list of risk factors that increase the chances of developing osteoporosis.

INHERENT RISK FACTORS:

- **GENDER:** Women are much more likely than men to develop osteoporosis, due to their smaller bone density and the physical impact of menopause.

- **AGE:** Bones grow weaker over time, and the risk of developing osteoporosis increases with age.

- **BODY SIZE:** Smaller framed women have a greater risk of developing the disease.

- **ETHNICITY:** Caucasian and Asian women are more likely than African American and Hispanic women to develop osteoporosis.

- **FAMILY HISTORY:** Bone mass tends to be transmitted genetically. Those with a family history of osteoporosis, bone fractures, and other bone disorders should pay extra attention to their bone health.

CHANGEABLE RISK FACTORS:

- **CALCIUM AND VITAMIN D INTAKE:** Up your intake of both nutrients to limit bone loss over time.

- **INACTIVITY:** A lack of exercise weakens bones over time; increase daily activity to strengthen bones.

- **SMOKING:** Interferes with the Vitamin D/Calcium Absorption process.

- **ALCOHOL INTAKE:** Interferes with the body's natural bone reconstruction process.

Prevention of Skeletal Disorders

Regular exercise, especially weight bearing exercise, is important for strengthening and maintaining bone density. This type of exercise includes running, jogging, brisk walking, hiking, weight lifting, field sports, tennis, Pilates, yoga, and dance.

Eating a diet high in calcium, vitamin K, magnesium, and potassium, and receiving adequate levels of vitamin D are good for the skeletal system. Vitamin D intake is also extremely important in children, who are prone to developing the bone-softening disease Rickets, if undernourished. Adding a quick, delicious, bone-friendly **NUTRIBLAST** to your day is a perfect way to easily get the nutrition needed to replenish the strength of your bones.

Sunlight also plays a huge role in our skeletal health, as it helps the body produce the vitamin D needed to absorb calcium. Moderate exposure to sunlight (10 to 60 minutes per week, depending on skin color) helps the body manufacture the nutrient.

If you smoke, quit. Also reduce alcohol consumption to at most 10 drinks a week for men, 5 for women.

Did you know?

The clavicle—or collarbone—is the most frequently broken bone in people.

Blasting for
Healthy Skeletal System

Just one **NUTRIBLAST** a day can supply your body with exceptional plant-based calcium, vitamin K, magnesium, and potassium it needs to maintain healthy bones. PLUS, extracting leafy greens, nuts, and other fruits and vegetables in the **NUTRIBULLET** makes nutrients bioavailable for maximum absorption into your system!

Top Foods for Bone Health

1. Collard Greens, turnip greens, mustard greens, spinach, kale

All of these vegetables are excellent sources of both calcium and vitamin K. For those under 30, proper calcium intake is key to building strong, healthy bones.
For those over 30, it's important to get plenty of food-based calcium into the bloodstream so the body will not deplete bone reserves as quickly.

The vitamin K in these green vegetables has been shown to slow bone loss associated with aging. It also helps to strengthen bones, protecting them against fracture and other injury. Just one serving of any of these vegetables provides more (in some cases, 10 times more!) than the daily-required value of vitamin K.

2. Wheat bran, cashews, spinach, almonds, cacao

All of these foods are good sources of magnesium. Like calcium, magnesium is stored in bone, contributes to skeletal strength, and is released from the bones by osteoclast breakdown into the blood stream to assist other bodily functions. In addition to strengthening bone structures, magnesium also supports healthy muscular and immune function, regulates blood pressure, and helps the body metabolize energy and synthesize protein. It is important that the body receive enough magnesium to slow the bone breakdown process, especially as we age.

3. Swiss chard, lima beans, sweet potato, spinach, papaya

All of these foods contain high levels of potassium, which neutralizes acids in the body known to eat away at bone tissue. Potassium is especially important if you eat a lot of citrus or tomato, as both foods are acidic and can contribute to bone loss.

Healthy Skeleton Blast

Berry Bone Builder

- -50% kale
- -1 banana
- -1/2 cup raspberries
- -1/2 cup blueberries
- -1/4 cup wheat bran
- -10 Cashews
- -2 tbs raw cacao
- -water: top with water to MAX LINE and extract

Papaya Punch

- -50% Swiss chard
- -1 cup papaya
- -1/2 steamed sweet potato
- -10 almonds
- -1 tsp of cinnamon
- -water: top with water to MAX LINE and extract

Skeleton Strengthener

- -25% spinach
- -25% collard greens
- -1 banana
- -1/2 cup blackberries
- -1/2 cup strawberries
- -2 tbs raw cacao powder or nibs, or 5 cacao beans
- -water: top with water to MAX LINE and extract

Calci-Yum

- -50% spinach
- -1 banana
- -1/2 orange
- -10 almonds
- -chia or flax seeds
- -1 tbs blackstrap molasses
- -water: top with water to MAX LINE and extract

Vitamin K-razy

- -25% mustard greens
- -25% turnip greens
- -1/2 banana
- -1 cup papaya
- -1/2 orange (or 1 mandarin)
- -1/4 cup pumpkin seeds
- -2 tbs raw cacao
- -water: top with water to MAX LINE and extract

The Bone Up Blast
- -25 % Swiss chard
- -25% kale
- -1/2 apple
- -1/2 pear
- -1/2 cup blueberries
- -10 cashews
- -1/4 cup goji berries
- -2 tbs raw cacao powder, nibs, or beans
- -water: top with water to MAX LINE and extract

Mega Magnesium
- -50% spinach
- -1/2 avocado
- -1 cup papaya
- -1/2 cup broccoli
- -1/4 cup wheat bran
- -10 cashews
- -2 tbs raw cacao powder or nibs, or 5 cacao beans
- -water: top with water to MAX LINE and extract

Bone Chiller
- -25% spinach
- -25% kale
- -1/2 avocado
- -½ orange
- -12 almonds
- -1 oz chia seeds
- -almond milk: top with almond milk to MAX LINE and extract

Muscular System

Role of the Muscular System

The muscular system makes body movement and balance possible, maintains the standing neutral spine position, generates heat, and makes up the tissues of the heart responsible for circulating blood and lymph throughout the body.

Muscles work directly with the nervous system, as they are moved—or contracted—by electrical nerve impulses. These impulses can be voluntary (consciously decided) or involuntary (automatically performed). They play a huge role in the function of other organ systems, as the following section illustrates.

Components of the Muscular System

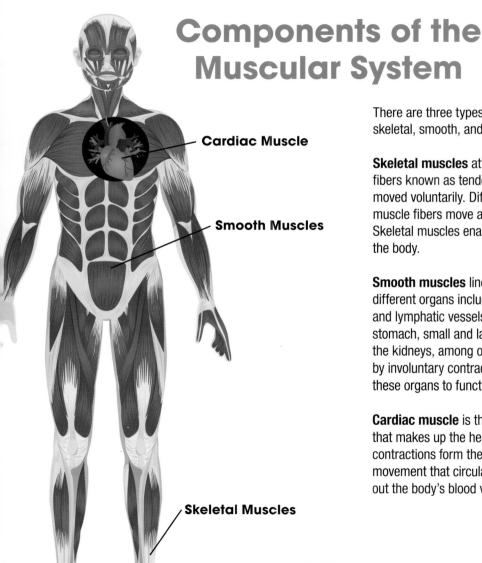

Cardiac Muscle

Smooth Muscles

Skeletal Muscles

There are three types of muscle: skeletal, smooth, and cardiac muscle.

Skeletal muscles attach to bone with fibers known as tendons and can be moved voluntarily. Different skeletal muscle fibers move at different paces. Skeletal muscles enable movement in the body.

Smooth muscles line the walls of different organs including the blood and lymphatic vessels, urinary bladder, stomach, small and large intestines, and the kidneys, among others. They move by involuntary contractions, allowing these organs to function automatically.

Cardiac muscle is the muscle tissue that makes up the heart. Cardiac muscle contractions form the heartbeat—a movement that circulates blood through-out the body's blood vessels.

www.nutribullet.com

Risk Factors for the Muscular System

Skeletal muscles are prone to fatigue, strains, sprains and tears, and must be warmed up before strenuous use. Those who engage in heavy lifting, intense exercise or any activity that stresses the skeletal muscles risk injury. Strained muscles are overworked and will spasm, knot or cramp. Sprained muscles involve torn tendons and/or ligaments, and will swell and bruise at the site of injury

Dehydration and electrolyte imbalance can cause skeletal muscles to cramp, and slow the muscle recovery process after strenuous exercise.

Smooth muscle problems often involve a miscommunication between nerve impulses and muscle contraction. These are more serious and harder to treat than most skeletal muscle problems. Smooth muscle issues often result from brain injury, including stroke. Factors that influence the smooth muscle/nerve connection include both diet and lifestyle choices, and those who drink excessively, smoke, and follow a high fat, high cholesterol, low-nutrient diet are more at risk than others for developing such issues.

Did you know?
The human body contains over 600 different muscles.

Like those involving smooth muscles, problems regarding cardiac muscle functioning can have dangerous, even deadly effects. Cardiac muscle disorders are known as cardiomyopathy and can be caused by a variety of circumstances including inflammation, blockage of blood supply (via blocked blood vessels), and weakening of the muscle fibers themselves. Like most life-threatening disorders, diet and lifestyle play a huge role in determining the health of the heart and its muscle tissues. Alcohol and exercise, in particular, seem to greatly impact cardiac muscle health. Excess alcohol consumption, as well as a lack of physical activity can greatly weaken cardiac muscle.

Common Muscle Disorders

Skeletal Muscle Problems
Cramps, sprain, strain, tear, muscular dystrophy, tumors

Smooth Muscle Problems
Amyotrophic Lateral Sclerosis (Lou Gehrig's Disease), stroke, Huntington's disease, multiple sclerosis, tumors

Cardiac Muscle Problems
Cardiomyopathy: can be extrinsic—caused by a symptom outside of the heart that caused the muscle to weaken or intrinsic—the weakening of the muscle in itself

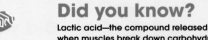

Did you know?
Lactic acid—the compound released when muscles break down carbohydrate molecules for energy—can cause muscle soreness during strenuous activity, but also serves as additional fuel for the body during long periods of exercise. When lactic acid fuel kicks in, exercisers feel their "second wind."

Preventing Muscle Disorders

As with most health problems, the risk of developing muscle disorders can be greatly reduced by following a healthy diet, exercising, and refraining from smoking, drinking, and using illicit drugs. Because muscles are present in many different organs and organ systems, care for one's overall health can have a positive effect on the different tissues of the muscular system.

Risk of experiencing less serious problems involving skeletal muscles like cramps, spasms, strains, and sprains can be reduced with proper hydration and electrolyte balance, as well as warm-ups before and stretches after strenuous exercise or heavy lifting.

Improving Muscle Development

Nutrition is just as important for strengthening muscles as it is for preventing muscle disorders. It is important to fully hydrate and nourish your body before and after physical exercise. Fueling your muscles with proper nutrition can build your endurance and decrease your recovery time, allowing you to exercise longer and more frequently to increase your fitness level.

Blasting for a Healthy Muscular System

The **NUTRIBULLET** is your best tool for absorbing all the nourishing, muscle building and healing nutrients you need. One **NUTRIBLAST** a day can deliver vitamin K, potassium, antioxidants, and omega 3 fatty acids from your favorite plant foods to keep all your muscles in top form!

Top Foods for Muscle Health:

1. **Collard Greens, turnip greens, mustard greens, spinach, kale**
   All contain calcium and vitamin K, which encourage skeletal muscle movement and reduce fatigue.

2. **Swiss chard, lima beans, sweet potato, spinach, papaya**
   Contain potassium, an essential electrolyte known to regulate the body's hydration levels, and prevent muscle cramps and spasms.

3. **Spinach, blueberries, cherries, almonds**
   These foods all contain flavonoids and antioxidants, both of which work to reduce inflammation in the body. This is especially helpful with sprained muscles, that swell and ache as they repair.

4. **Walnuts, avocado, olive oil, flax seeds, chia seeds**
   All contain omega-3 fatty acids, that lower levels of artery-clogging triglycerides in the blood. This is especially helpful in preventing cardiomyopathy (heart muscle disease). Omega-3's have also been shown to improve overall brain health, which may reduce one's risk of developing neuromuscular conditions.

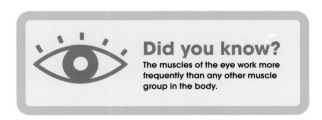

Did you know?
The muscles of the eye work more frequently than any other muscle group in the body.

Muscle Blasts

Flex Factor
- 50% collard greens
- 1/2 avocado
- 1 cup papaya
- 1/2 cup cherries
- 10 walnut halves
- 1 tbs chia seeds
- water: top with water to MAX LINE and extract

Blue Builder
- 50% spinach
- 1/2 avocado
- 1 cup blueberries
- 12 almonds
- 1 tbs flax seeds
- water or almond milk: top with water or almond milk to MAX LINE and extract

Sweet Success
- 50% kale
- 1 cup steamed sweet potato
- 1 cup cherries
- 12 almonds
- 1 tbs olive oil
- water or almond milk: top with water or almond milk to MAX LINE and extract

Muscle Meal
- 25% spinach
- 25% collard greens
- 1/2 avocado
- 1/2 banana
- 1 cup papaya
- 8 walnut halves
- 5 almonds
- water: top with water to MAX LINE and extract

Lima Lean
- 50% Swiss Chard
- 1/2 avocado
- 1 cup raw lima beans (can be frozen)
- 1 cup papaya
- 10 almonds
- 1 tbs chia seeds
- water or almond milk: top with water or almond milk to MAX LINE and extract

Strong to the Finish
- 50% spinach
- 1 banana
- 10 walnut halves
- 1 tbs flax seeds
- water or almond milk: top with water or almond milk to MAX LINE and extract

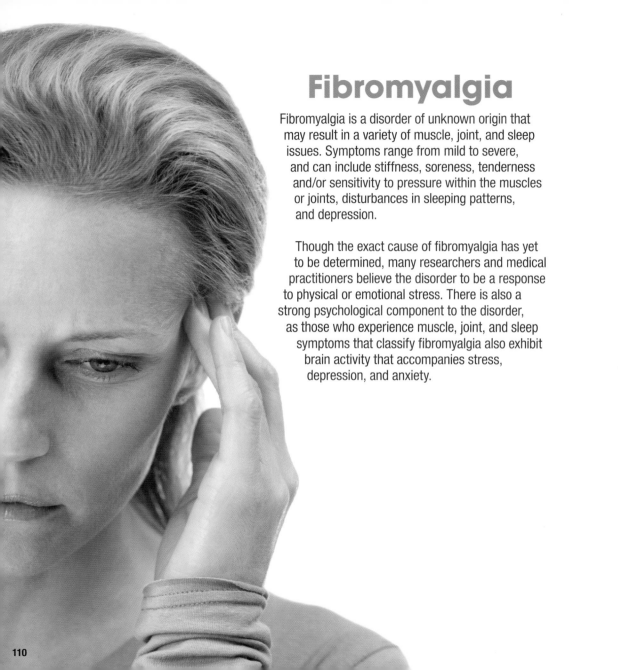

Fibromyalgia

Fibromyalgia is a disorder of unknown origin that may result in a variety of muscle, joint, and sleep issues. Symptoms range from mild to severe, and can include stiffness, soreness, tenderness and/or sensitivity to pressure within the muscles or joints, disturbances in sleeping patterns, and depression.

Though the exact cause of fibromyalgia has yet to be determined, many researchers and medical practitioners believe the disorder to be a response to physical or emotional stress. There is also a strong psychological component to the disorder, as those who experience muscle, joint, and sleep symptoms that classify fibromyalgia also exhibit brain activity that accompanies stress, depression, and anxiety.

Fibromyalgia Risk Factors

Sex: women account for 90% of all fibromyalgia sufferers.

Family History: One third of all fibromyalgia sufferers have a parent with fibromyalgia

Stress: Those who live in a stressful environment, or are especially susceptible to both physical and emotional stress are at higher risk of developing symptoms of fibromyalgia

Age: Fibromyalgia symptoms surface most frequently in middle age, but patients' ages tend to range from 20 to 60 years old.

Diet: Certain foods are thought to intensify fibromyalgia symptoms. These include dairy, caffeine, nightshade vegetables (eggplant, potatoes, tomatoes, peppers), fried foods, salted/pickled foods, alcohol, refined flours, and added sugars

Treatment

Conventional treatment methods involve prescribed painkillers and/or antidepressants, as well as cognitive-behavioral therapy. While these treatments can be helpful, many patients have also experienced both physical and emotional relief from fibromyalgia symptoms by eliminating processed foods and dairy products from their diet, and increasing consumption of plant foods. Specifically, omega-3 fatty acids found in salmon and walnuts (among other foods) and antioxidant-dense fruits and vegetables like berries and leafy greens have shown to assist with the symptoms of fibromyalgia.

Blasting To Fight Fibromyalgia

1. Apples, apple cider vinegar, pears, pineapple, grapes

These foods all contain malic acid, a natural compound that plays a vital role in cellular energy production. Malic acid, when consumed with magnesium, has shown to decrease the symptoms of fibromyalgia.

2. Seeds, nuts, legumes, dark green vegetables like kale, collards, spinach, and broccoli

All of these foods contain magnesium, which has shown to reduce the intensity of the body's stress response, a physical and neurological process that can trigger fibromyalgia symptoms. Magnesium is especially effective when consumed with foods containing malic acid.

3. Almonds, flax seeds, soybeans, garbanzo beans, collard greens, and sunflower seeds

These foods all contain tryptophan, an amino acid used to manufacture melatonin in the brain. When released, melatonin regulates hormonal changes and sleep rhythms, which can both be compromised in patients with fibromyalgia.

4. Ginger, turmeric, flax seeds, chia seeds, avocado

All of these foods help to fight inflammation—a contributing factor in the muscular and skeletal pain that accompanies fibromyalgia. Specifically, ginger contains compounds called gingerols, turmeric contains circumins, and flax, chia, and avocado all contain Omega-3 fatty acids—all of which are powerful anti-inflammatories.

5. Maca Root

This South American superfood has been used for millennia to improve stamina and fight fatigue in the high-altitude Andes mountain range, making it an excellent energizer for those suffering from fibromyalgia fatigue. You can find powdered maca in the U.S. at most health food stores.

Best Fibromyalgia-Fighting Blasts

Morning Star
- -2 handfuls spinach
- -1 banana
- -1/8 cup pumpkin seeds
- -1 orange (peeled)
- -1 carrot
- -1-2 Tbsp plant-protein powder
  (spirulina, pea, hemp, rice, soy)
- -Water or dairy alternative (almond, soy, rice milks):
  top with water or dairy alternative to
  MAX LINE and extract

Inflammation Alleviation
- -2 handfuls kale
- -1/2 avocado
- -1/4 cup gluten-free rolled oats
- -1 Tbsp flax seeds
- -1 cored apple
- -1 handful of blueberries
- -Water or dairy alternative (almond, soy, rice milks):
  top with water or dairy alternative to MAX LINE and extract

Macarita
- -2 handfuls of chard
- -1 banana
- -1/8 cup of almonds
- -1-2 Tbsp plant-protein powder (spirulina, pea, hemp, rice, soy)
- -1-2 tps maca powder
- -Water or dairy alternative (almond, soy, rice milks):
  top with water or dairy alternative to MAX LINE and extract

Malic-Magnesium Elysium
- -2 handfuls collards
- -½ avocado
- -½ apple, cored
- -½ pear, cored
- -1/8 cup sunflower seeds
- -Water or dairy alternative (almond, soy,
  rice milks): top with water or dairy
  alternative to MAX LINE and extract

Foods for Detoxification

Our bodies take in a huge amount of toxins each day. From bus fumes to alcohol, cigarette smoke to processed food, substances containing free radicals and other destructive compounds constantly enter our system and can **wreak havoc** on our health.

Fortunately, there are plenty of foods and natural remedies known both to repair damaged cells and eliminate toxic particles from the body. The latter is known as detoxification, and primarily involves the liver and kidneys, though other organs play secondary roles.

If we detox a bit everyday, we reduce the risk of collecting toxic buildup in our bodies, which can cause permanent and long-lasting damage.

The Liver

The liver filters the blood and collects dead cells, damaging chemicals, and harmful microorganisms. It then uses specific enzymes to kill, break down, and/or neutralize these substances so they can be safely reabsorbed by the blood stream and transported to the kidneys. The liver also serves important digestive functions, as highlighted in the digestion portion of this book.

The Kidneys

Often described as blood cleaners, kidneys receive filtered blood from the liver, and filter it again, reabsorbing vital nutrients and water back into the bloodstream, and eliminating any excess compounds through the urine, which flows through the **ureters,** collects in the **bladder** and is expelled from the body through the **urethra.**

Blasting to Detoxify

Eliminating toxins taken in from the environment is key to maintaining a healthy body. Drink antioxidant-rich foods in your **NUTRIBLASTS** and supercharge your health by protecting your liver and kidneys from free radicals!

Best Foods for Detoxing

1. Beets and beet greens

Known for their cleansing properties, beets are loaded with powerful antioxidants that help detoxify the liver and kidneys. Extract them raw to maximize their benefits.

Nutrients from extracted beets are readily absorbed by the body, and may cause nausea if consumed too quickly. Mix with other vegetables like carrot or cabbage. If you must drink extracted beets alone, do not consume more than 4 oz at a time, and dilute with at least 2 oz of water.

2. Celery

Loaded with antioxidants and celebrated for its diuretic properties, celery is an excellent detoxifying ingredient. It is especially beneficial to the kidneys, as it lowers uric acid levels in the blood, thus reducing an individual's risk of developing kidney stones. It makes a delicious and refreshing beverage when extracted with apple and lemon.

3. Artichokes

Like celery, artichokes lower blood uric acid levels. They also contain compounds that assist in the production and elimination of bile—the fluid discharge of toxins that the liver produces. This helps ensure that toxins are efficiently condensed and removed from the body.

4. Apples

Research suggests that the antioxidants in apples may prevent the growth of cancer cells in the bowel and liver.

5. Greens: spinach, alfalfa, spirulina, chlorella, arugula, wheat grass

Full of chlorophyll, these greens help the liver rid the body of harmful dietary and environmental toxins, especially pesticides, heavy metals, smog, and herbicides.

6. Garlic

This pungent bulb helps support the liver by producing enzymes that filter toxins from the digestive tract. Enjoy raw or cooked.

7. Asparagus, broccoli, cauliflower, carrots, turmeric, oregano

Full of sulfur and glutathione, these foods helps in the detoxification process, especially when eaten raw.

8. Citrus Fruits

Rich in vitamin C, these foods transform harmful toxins into digestable material. They also support the liver cleansing process.

9. Green Tea

Green tea is loaded with many antioxidants, including catechins—chemical compounds renowned for their detoxifying properties.

Detoxifying Blasts

Toxin Tamer
- 50% beet greens
- 2 stalks celery
- 1 lemon, peeled
- 1 pinch of cayenne pepper
- water: fill to MAX LINE and extract

Pure at Heart (enjoy this blast as a chilled soup)
- 50% spinach
- 1 cup steamed artichoke hearts
- 1 clove garlic
- 1 pinch turmeric
- lemon juice squeezed from ½ lemon
- water: fill to MAX LINE and extract

Celerade
- 3 stalks celery
- juice from 1 lemon, peeled
- 1 apple, seeds removed
- water: fill to MAX LINE and extract

Green Machine
- 25% spinach
- 25% arugula
- 2 stalks celery
- juice of 1 lemon
- 1 chlorella or spirulina tablet
- chilled unsweetened green tea: fill to the MAX FILL LINE and extract

Beet Treat
- 50% spinach
- 1 beet, cut into cubes
- 1 apple, seeds removed
- 1 lemon, peeled
- water: fill to MAX LINE and extract

Ginger Kale
- 50% kale
- 1 apple
- 1 lemon, peeled
- one 1" slice of ginger, peeled
- water: fill to MAX LINE and extract

Veg Out
- 50% spinach
- 1 head of broccoli
- 3 spears of asparagus
- 1 apple, cut into chunks
- water: fill to the MAX FILL LINE and extract

TeaTox
- 50% arugula
- handful of alfalfa sprouts or wheat grass
- 1 orange, peeled
- 1 lemon, peeled
- chilled unsweetened green tea: fill to the MAX FILL LINE and extract

Foods for Sleep

Sleep plays a huge role in personal health. Maintaining a regular sleep schedule gives the body time to rest and rejuvenate. Cells grow, wounds heal faster, memory sharpens, and muscles repair and strengthen when the body receives adequate sleep. While researchers make new discoveries about the purposes of sleep every day, the fact that every living animal sustains its own sleep cycle suggests that sleep is hugely important for all walks of life.

zᶻᶻ

Did you know?
Staying awake for over 17 hours impairs your brain functioning the same amount as having a blood alcohol content of .05%.

5 STAGES of SLEEP

LIGHT SLEEP 1
Muscles begin to relax.
A person drifts in and out and
can be easily awakened.

LIGHT SLEEP 2
Brain waves slow down,
then occasionally speed
up in small bursts called
sleep spindles; eye
movement stops.

SLEEP CYCLE

REM SLEEP
Limbs become temporarily
paralyzed, eye movement
increases, breathing
accelerates, sleepers start
dreaming (if they haven't
begun at previous stages).

DEEP SLEEP 1
Brain waves continue to
slow down, producing
low-level delta waves;
these waves are
periodically interrupted
with faster waves.

DEEP SLEEP 2
Delta waves dominate
brain activity; eye
movement and
muscle activity
is minimal.

While the amount of sleep needed differs between individuals, most adults function best on 7-8 hours of sleep. The sleep cycle will repeat roughly four times in an eight-hour sleep.

What Happens When We Don't Get Enough Sleep:
Everyone experiences the occasional bout of insomnia (sleeplessness). As long as sleeplessness does not occur for more than three nights in a row, the worst you'll experience is grouchiness or fatigue during the day. After three restless nights, however, body systems become compromised: mental agility slows, moods change, and the immune system weakens. Getting a good night's sleep is very important to proper bodily function and long term health.

Sleep Disorders

Chronic Insomnia

Chronic insomnia—sleeplessness that occurs for most nights over a one-month period of time—affects nearly 10% of Americans. It often results from psychological conditions like depression or anxiety, and physical maladies like asthma, arthritis, or digestive disorders. Inadequate vitamin intake, excess caffeine, alcohol, nicotine, or narcotic intake, and prescription medications can also inhibit sleep for extended periods of time.

Restless Leg Syndrome

Restless Leg Syndrome is a neurological disorder that prompts an uncontrollable urge to move one's limbs. This urge is usually (but not always) accompanied by a sensation in the limbs, whether itching, tingling, or muscle tightness, and causes the limbs to kick, twitch, and/or jerk involuntarily. Sensations can be mild to severe, and usually start at night, when the body begins to relax for bed. Because it is so physically demanding, Restless Leg Syndrome often prevents the sufferer from falling asleep, or wakes him or her up while (s)he is sleeping. This lack of sleep results in poor performance, drowsiness, and irritability during the day. If RLS prevents sleep for more than a month, symptoms of chronic insomnia may occur.

Nutrient deficiency is often cited as a cause of RLS—specifically deficiencies of iron, magnesium, or folate. It has also been linked to autoimmune disorders, diabetes, and Parkinson's disease, among others.

Z^{zz} **Did you know?**
On average, humans sleep three hours less than other primates.

Sleep Apnea

Sleep apnea inhibits normal breath during sleep, which results in oxygen deprivation and causing sufferers to awaken suddenly, gasping for air. Sufferers may not remember waking up at any point during the night, but will experience symptoms of insomnia like sluggishness, lack of focus, and moodiness. Depression may result, as sufferers cannot identify the cause of these issues.

Sleep Apnea is associated with serious medical conditions like high blood pressure, stroke, and heart disease. Sleep apnea can also greatly inhibit a person's REM (dream) sleep, and in doing so, has been linked to an increased risk of developing extreme psychological disorders. Obesity increases a person's risk of experiencing sleep apnea, as excess fat inhibits the diaphragm from fully expanding.

Preventing Sleep Problems

Diet, nutrition, and eating patterns have a large effect on sleep quality. Foods and drinks contain compounds that can either keep you up at night, or help you sleep soundly. Mealtime also plays a role in a person's sleep cycle. As a general rule of thumb, stop eating at least two hours before going to bed, and do not consume caffeine, smoke cigarettes, or ingest any other stimulants after 2:00 in the afternoon.

The following section explains how extracting nutrient-dense foods in the **NUTRIBULLET** can significantly improve your sleep and restore your body's vital energy.

Did you know?

Falling asleep within five minutes of lying down indicates sleep deprivation. Individuals with a healthy sleep cycle generally take 10-15 minutes to fully nod off.

Blasting for a Better Night's Sleep

Best Foods for a Better Night's Sleep

1. **Dates, cashews, oats, spirulina, pumpkin seeds, and sunflower seeds**
   These foods all contain an amino acid called tryptophan that releases chemicals melatonin and serotonin in the brain. Both chemicals give the body a happy, drowsy feeling, and play a large role in maintaining the sleep cycle.

2. **Pumpkin seeds, swiss chard, spinach**
   These foods all contain high magnesium levels—a mineral known to relax the muscles, strengthen the bones, and encourage blood flow (circulation) to all areas of the body. Healthy muscles, bones, and circulation can relax more readily at bedtime. Due to its role in muscle relaxation, magnesium is linked to Restless Leg Syndrome. Increasing magnesium intake may help prevent instances of the condition.

3. **Turnip greens, mustard greens, collard greens**
   These greens are all excellent sources of calcium, which plays a large role in sustaining REM sleep. After observing an increase in calcium levels in the body during this sleep stage, experts have concluded that calcium helps the brain process tryptophan to release melatonin, a substance known to increase peaceful drowsiness.

Did you know?
Exposure to LED light rays from alarm clocks and other electronic devices can prevent individuals from entering deep sleep.

Blasts for a
Better Night's Sleep

Sleepy Pie
-1/4 cup cooked oatmeal
-2 dates
-12 cashews
-1 tsp cinnamon
-almond milk: top with almond milk to
 MAX LINE and extract

Sleepy Seeds
-50% spinach
-1 Banana
-Raspberry
-Blueberry
-1 tbs pumpkin seeds
-1 tbs sunflower seeds
-water: top with water to MAX LINE
 and extract

Deep Green Sleep
-50% collard greens
-1/2 avocado
-1 carrot, peeled
-1 tomato
-1 lemon (peeled)
-1 tsp spirulina
-1 pinch of Sea Salt
-water: top with water to MAX LINE
 and extract

Veg Out
-50% Swiss chard
-1 peeled carrot
-1 stalk celery, cut into pieces
-1 tomato
-1 lemon, peeled
-2 tbs sunflower Seeds
-water: top with water to MAX LINE and extract

Spinach Slumber
-50% Spinach
-1 banana
-1/2 cup mixed Berries
-12 cashews
-water: top with water to MAX LINE and extract

Bedtime Blast
-50% spinach
-1 cup watermelon
-1/4 cup pumpkin seeds
-water: top with water to MAX LINE and extract

Nightcap
-1 banana
-1 medjool date
-1 fig
-12 cashews
-almond milk: top with almond milk to
 MAX LINE and extract

Foods for Healthful Aging

No one knows exactly what causes us to age, though a long list of scientific theories attempt to explain the phenomenon. Proposed causes range from the reproduction of damaged cells over time to the deregulation of reproductive hormones, to the accumulation of free radical damage as we grow older. While precise reasons for aging have yet to be determined, it is well known that living a healthy lifestyle can greatly improve the length and quality of a person's life.

Age is not simply defined by the number of years a person has lived. It is also determined by a person's biological health—the resilience of cells within the body. While we can't stop or turn back the hands of time, there are many diet and lifestyle choices we can make to delay cell deterioration and keep ourselves strong and vital into old age. Illness, infection, malnutrition and environmental toxins can speed up the aging process, while proper—even "super"—nutrition, daily exercise, hydration, and reduced exposure to toxic substances can delay, and possibly reverse some signs of aging.

Did you know?

Japan has the longest life expectancy in the world—78.5 years for men and 85.5 years for women! Many attribute this to their traditional diet of fish, sea vegetables, rice and non-genetically modified soy.

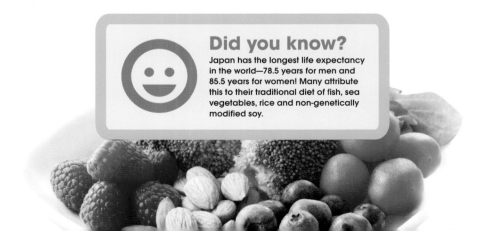

Age Accelerators

Free Radicals

There are many theories regarding aging. Recently, much medical attention has been paid to the strong link between the intake of free radicals and the speed of the aging process. Free radicals can damage the DNA of healthy cells, which not only ruins the specific cell, but also interferes with that cell's ability to regenerate. This damage produces weak cells that fail to protect the body, or mutated cells that cause illness and disease.

Free radicals can also lead to chronic inflammation, a constant state of bodily stress that can weaken the immune system, making the body more prone to contracting illnesses.

Free radicals enter our system through chemically processed food (especially processed meat), cigarette smoke, alcohol, drugs, and environmental pollutants. Avoiding these substances as much as possible can have a large impact on the rate at which we age.

Malabsorption

No matter how healthy a person's diet, if he or she cannot absorb nutrients through the digestive tract and into the bloodstream, the body will not receive what it needs to run properly. Without adequate nutrition, cell activity slows and eventually stops, causing cells to die and the body to age. Every decade our stomach enzymes become 10% less effective in breaking down our food, making it increasingly difficult for our bodies to receive the nutrients it needs as we age. This is why eating nutrition extracted food is SO excellent for our bodies. With the **NUTRIBULLET,** you can be sure that you are getting the best nutrition possible, no matter how many years you haved lived!

Inactivity

Doctors, scientists, and holistic healers all agree on the importance of leading an active lifestyle. Proper exercise—defined as at least twenty-five minutes of moderate to vigorous aerobic activity (brisk walking, jogging, field sports, biking) each day, and resistance training (weight lifting, resistance bands, Pilates, yoga) twice a week by the Centers for Disease Control—increases the amount of oxygen taken in by the body, which energizes the cells. Moderate exercise also puts a beneficial amount pressure on the muscles and joints, which strengthens their resilience.

Aging

Slowing the Aging Process

Maintaining one's general health is extremely important for sustaining healthy cell growth and regeneration. The longer individuals live a healthy lifestyle, the slower their aging process will be. It is, however, never too late to reap the benefits proper nutrition and exercise can offer.

While overall health is important, there are specific foods known as "superfoods" that contain powerful antioxidants shown to fight free radicals, halt cell damage and even regenerate old cells that have long been inactive.

Blasting For Anti-Aging

1. **Red apples, nectarines, blackberries, blueberries, raspberries, black and green tea**
   These foods all contain bioflavonoid antioxidants that reduce inflammation, prevent cancer, protect the brain and guard cells from the wear and tear of aging.

2. **Split peas, artichokes, white beans, black beans, garbanzo beans**
   All are good sources of plant-based protein. The body loses muscle as it ages, making it exceptionally important to include sufficient amounts of protein in the diet. Lost muscle weakens the body and makes beneficial activities such as cardiovascular and weight-bearing exercise increasingly difficult.

3. **Flax seeds, walnuts**
   These two super foods are fantastic sources of DHA Omega-3 fatty acids, which have anti-inflammatory properties and have been linked to improved brain function and the delayed onset of neurological aging.

Extracting your fruits, vegetables, nuts and seeds in the **NUTRIBULLET** will flood your body with the nutrients it needs to stay in optimal health. Drink one **NUTRIBLAST** a day, and regain your strength and vitality—you'll feel years younger!

Anti-Aging Blasts

Fountain of Youth
- 50% spinach
- 1/2 avocado
- 1 medium nectarine
- 1/2 cup blueberries
- 10 walnut halves
- water: top with water to MAX LINE and extract

Sweet Pea
- 50% butter lettuce
- 1 banana
- 1/2 cup raspberries
- 1/2 cup green peas
- 1 tbs flax seed
- water: top with water to MAX LINE and extract

Tea Time
- 50% butter lettuce
- 1 banana
- 1 cup blackberries
- 1 tbs flax seed
- green or black tea: top with chilled green or black tea to MAX LINE and extract

Berry Buddy
- 50% kale
- 1/2 avocado
- 1/2 cup blueberries
- 1/2 cup blackberries
- 1/2 cup raspberries
- water or almond milk: top with water or almond milk to MAX LINE and extract

Staying Power
- 50% Swiss chard
- 1 banana
- 1/2 cup strawberries
- 1/2 cup blueberries
- 1/2 cup white beans
- 1 tbs flax seed
- water: top with water to MAX LINE and extract

Life Line
- 50% kale
- 1/2 avocado
- 1 cup artichoke hearts
- 1/2 cup white beans
- 1/2 tomato
- Juice of 1/2 lemon
- 10 walnut halves
- water: top with water to MAX LINE and extract

Apple a Day
- 50% spinach
- 1/2 avocado
- 1 red apple, cored and cut into chunks
- 10 walnut halves
- 2 tsp cinnamon
- water or almond milk: top with water or almond milk to MAX LINE and extract

Foods for Beauty

While beauty is very much in the eye of the beholder, there are several traits that seem to be generally acknowledged as appealing. Clear skin, strong teeth, bright eyes, and shiny hair signify health and wellness, which are attractive traits regardless of individual or cultural preferences.

What to avoid

Those looking for a glowing appearance should avoid smoking, refined sugar, and processed foods. The chemicals in cigarette smoke narrow blood vessels in the top layer of your skin, which limits the blood flow, and thus, the transportation of nutrients to those areas. This causes premature aging and wrinkles. Cigarette smoke also yellows the teeth, and may reduce the body's overall nutrient absorption.

Refined sugars cause inflammation in the body, which may result in acne and gum disease. They also contribute to tooth decay.

Highly processed foods also cause inflammation, and lack the enzymes that skin, hair, and nail cells need to grow and regenerate.

Did you know?

Drinking 3 cups of oolong tea a day can suppress symptoms of the inflammatory skin disorder eczema.

Blasting for Beauty

Extracting foods in the **NUTRIBULLET** releases vital nutrients to give you glowing skin, a bright smile, shiny hair, and sparkling eyes. Incorporate **NUTRIBLASTS** into your daily regime, and see the natural beauty that radiates from extracted nutrition!

Best Foods for Beauty

1. Grapes, strawberries, pineapple
Use these three fruits as topical skin exfoliants, as they contain alpha hydroxyl acids that help dissolve the dead skin cells that clog oil glands and cause pimples, whiteheads, and blackheads. Eating all sorts of fruit in general is great for the skin, as fruit is both nutritionally dense and hydrating.

2. Almonds, beets, cashews, Swiss chard
While poisonous in larger quantities, small amounts of the oxalic acid contained in these foods have been shown to clear the skin and heal blemishes.

3. Apple cider vinegar
Apple cider vinegar is a natural tooth whitener and contains mild acids that remove stains from the teeth.

4. Barley, crimini mushrooms, Brazil nuts
These foods contain selenium, a mineral essential to immune function that can protect the body from cell damage. Sufficient selenium intake also encourages healthy thyroid functioning, which prompts the growth and regrowth of hair and nail cells.

5. Goji berries
Research has found a link between goji berries and the reversal of skin damage, particularly damage caused by sunburn and UV radiation.

Beauty Blasts

Beauty Bar
- 50% mixture of turnip, collard, and mustard greens
- 3 spears of tender young asparagus
- ½ apple
- ½ cup of blueberries
- 10 hazelnuts
- 2 tbs raw cacao powder
- water: top with water to MAX LINE and extract

Sipping Pretty
- 1/4 cup goji berries
- 1/4 cup almonds
- 2 tbs raw cacao
- 1 ½ cups almond milk
- Add all ingredients to the short cup and extract

Cider Cup
- 50% Swiss chard
- 1 cup red grapes
- 1/2 one raw beet
- 1 brazil nut
- 1 tablespoon apple cider vinegar
- water: top with water to MAX LINE and extract

Glow Profile
- 50% Swiss Chard
- 1/2 cup pineapple
- 1/2 cup strawberries
- 1 tbs goji berries
- 12 cashews
- water: top with water to MAX LINE and extract

Strawberry Scrub
Use this recipe as a facial scrub to heal pimples and unclog pores.
- 5 fresh strawberries
- 10 raw almonds
- 3 leaves swiss chard
- Pulse ingredients in short cup until roughly combined. Wet face, use as a facial scrub, and rinse with water

Did you know?
Good oral hygiene not only keeps your smile looking beautiful, but also may greatly reduce your risk of developing heart conditions by limiting the inflammatory stress on your body.

THE NUTRIBULLET SUPERFOOD
6-WEEK
TRANSFORMATION PLAN
Because Nothing Feels as Good as Feeling Good™

For those looking to seriously transform their health and their lives, look no further than this **THE SUPERFOOD 6-WEEK TRANSFORMATION PLAN!**

The next 60 pages are FULL of the meal plans, eating schedules, recipes, tips and tricks you need to overhaul your health and regain lost vitality.

People who have followed this plan have increased their energy, lost weight, and improved the way they look and feel all in just weeks!! Are you ready to do the same?

Turn the page to find out more!

WARNING!

- BEFORE BEGINNING THIS OR ANY OTHER DIETARY PROGRAM, PLEASE CONSULT WITH YOUR DOCTOR ESPECIALLY IF YOU ARE CURRENTLY TAKING ANY STATINS, OTHER CHOLESTEROL LOWERING MEDICATION, BLOOD THINNERS, BLOOD PRESSURE MEDICATION, ANTIDEPRESSANTS, OR OTHER PRESCRIPTION OR OVER THE COUNTER MEDICATION AS ANY CHANGE IN DIET CAN HAVE AN IMPACT ON THE AFFECT OF YOUR MEDICATION. YOU SHOULD NOT STOP TAKING YOUR MEDICATION WITHOUT CONSULTING YOUR DOCTOR. THE INFORMATION CONTAINED IN OUR GUIDE AND RECIPES IS NOT INTENDED TO TREAT OR CURE ANY DISEASE, BUT IS A PROGRAM TO MAINTAIN GOOD HEALTH. IT IS NOT A SUBSTITUTE FOR REGULAR AND PROPER MEDICAL CARE.
- THIS FOOD PROGRAM IS NOT INTENDED FOR USE BY MINORS, PREGNANT WOMEN, OR INDIVIDUALS WITH ANY TYPE OF HEALTH CONDITION. SUCH INDIVIDUALS ARE SPECIFICALLY WARNED TO SEEK PROFESSIONAL MEDICAL ADVICE PRIOR TO INITIATING ANY FORM OF WEIGHT LOSS EFFORT OR DIET REGIMEN.

THE NUTRIBULLET SUPERFOOD 6-WEEK TRANSFORMATION PLAN
Because Nothing Feels as Good as Feeling Good

In the next six weeks, you can dramatically improve the way you look and feel by doing one simple thing—adding **NUTRITION EXTRACTED** whole foods to your daily diet! Our easy-to-follow **6-WEEK TRANSFORMATION PLAN** gives you all the tools you need to revitalize your body. Separated into three 2-week long phases, the program gradually introduces more and more fresh, raw produce and wholesome ingredients to your lifestyle.

Each phase of this program rests firmly on the foundation of the **NUTRIBLAST**—the ultra-nutritious, tasty shake that is easy to make and even easier to drink! Chock full of fruit, greens, and goodness, **NUTRIBLASTS** only take seconds to make, and blast your body with optimal nutrition. As you progress in the Program, you will increase the number and nutritional density of the **NUTRIBLASTS** you drink.

The ease and portability of **NUTRIBLASTS** make the **SUPERFOOD 6-WEEK TRANSFORMATION PLAN SO EASY TO FOLLOW.** You'll be enjoying these nutritious "super meals" a few times a day without cooking or dirtying pots and pans. Clean up is a snap, and you won't believe how easy it is to take your **NUTRIBLAST** on the go! Work at an office? Work outside? No problem. Just twist on the To-Go lid and your life boosting super meal is ready for the road!

Worried that **NUTRIBLASTS** won't fill you up? Fear not! You will NEVER go hungry on the **SUPERFOOD 6-WEEK TRANSFORMATION PLAN** because in addition to **NUTRIBLASTS,** you ALSO get to enjoy delicious snacks, savory soups, zesty salads and **hearty dinners.** Simply follow the follow the Five to Thrive Keys to Success on the next page and soon you will truly learn that "nothing feels as good as feeling good!"

www.nutribullet.com

THE "FIVE TO THRIVE" KEYS TO SUCCESS

1 **EXTRACT Your Nutrients!**

2 **Eat WHOLE Foods!**

3 **COMBINE Your Foods Properly**

4 **Eat HALF RAW at All Meals**

5 **Indulge INTELLIGENTLY**

THE "FIVE TO THRIVE" KEYS TO SUCCESS

To get the **MOST** out of life, you need to get the **MOST** out of your food. The following 5 steps will get you on the fast track to optimum health throughout the three phases of your **6-WEEK LIFEBOOST PROGRAM:**

① Extract Your Nutrients!

We are what we eat? Not Entirely. We are what we absorb, and our bodies often fail to absorb the essential nutrients they need.

In our busy lives, we rarely take the time to eat healthy, and very few of us chew foods the way doctors recommend. Because of these habits, it becomes increasingly difficult for our bodies to digest and absorb what we eat. Depleted, overworked digestive enzymes coupled with stomach acids that weaken with age cannot break food down to the point where we can access and utilize the nutrition inside. In other words, we don't absorb most of the nutrition contained in our food.

In fact, statistics say that we absorb 10% fewer nutrients every ten years we age. By the time we reach the age of 50, we are only absorbing 50% of the foods (nutrients) we eat. And each year that passes we absorb less and less.

When our body is denied this essential nutrition day after day, week after week, we lose our vitality and become more vulnerable to sickness and chronic disease.

Fortunately, the NUTRIBULLET breaks down food to its most absorbable state, so it is basically pre-digested. This process is known as **NUTRITION EXTRACTION.** When you consume this nutrition-extracted food, you spare your system the work of breaking down dense and fibrous foods, allowing it to focus on absorbing the maximum amount of nutrients locked inside. This is how the **NUTRIBULLET** turns ordinary food into super food!

NUTRiBULLET

❷ Eat Whole Foods

Food, according to Mirriam-Webster's Dictionary, is any substance that enables one to live and grow—anything that nourishes. Based on this definition, hardly anything in the Standard American Diet can be considered food!

The standard American diet is largely made up of processed foods. These food-like substances contain added ingredients, such as salt, sugar, high fructose corn syrup, chemically altered preservatives and trans fats that serve no nutritional purpose in the body. In fact, many of these ingredients can actually destroy the body and ruin our health! All convenience foods are processed, so if you didn't make it yourself, chances are you can't eat it during this program.

Whole foods, on the other hand, are unprocessed foods. They do not contain ingredients that you cannot pronounce or substances your grandparents wouldn't recognize. They do not come in a box or squeezable tube or microwaveable tray. They are not artificially seasoned or covered in unhealthy sauce.

Whole foods are foods in their original form. They are whole grains, fruits, vegetables, beans, legumes and unprocessed meats. Whole foods contain huge amounts of antioxidant vitamins, minerals and phytochemicals that protect your body from free radicals and disease.

These are the foods we will eat for the next 6 weeks.

Sound intimidating? Have no fear. Our **SUPERFOOD 6-WEEK TRANSFORMATION PLAN** recipes are quick and easy to make, not to mention delicious! We are confident that you'll be thrilled with the fabulous recipes included in this program. Stick with our menu for six weeks and you will see first hand how eating **SUPERFOODS** improves your mood, energy, and life!

THE "FIVE TO THRIVE" KEYS TO SUCCESS

❸ Combine Your Foods Properly*

Most of us have been brought up with the idea that a wholesome meal contains one serving of protein, one of starch and one or two servings of vegetables. However, studies show that separate digestive enzymes break down proteins and carbohydrates, and when these enzymes enter your gut at the same time, they cancel out each other's effectiveness. This slows down your digestive process, leaving you tired, sluggish, bloated, gassy and uncomfortable. Who needs that?

So, never eat protein and starch together. Enjoy meals composed of starches and veggies or proteins and veggies. To make it simple, our plan suggests starch and salad for lunch and protein and salad for dinner. Pair salad vegetables with whole grain starches or starchy vegetables during the day, and eat salad vegetables with lean protein at night. You will notice a difference in how your body feels and performs!

Here is a list of **LIFEBOOST** friendly starches, salad vegetables (low-starch vegetables), and lean proteins to guide you through your program:

SALAD VEGETABLES LOW STARCH	STARCHES	LEAN PROTEINS
All leafy greens, artichoke, asparagus, sprouts, broccoli, brussels sprouts, cabbage, carrots, cauliflower, celery, cucumber, eggplant, jicama, leeks, mushrooms, onions, peppers, radishes, summer squash, tomato, zucchini	**Whole Grains:** whole wheat, brown rice, barley, quinoa, oats, wheat berry, bulgur wheat, popcorn, millet **Starchy Vegetables:** beets, potatoes, sweet potatoes, yams, corn, beans, butternut squash, acorn squash, parsnips, peas	**Poultry:** chicken breast, turkey breast **Seafood:** salmon, tilapia, halibut **Red Meat:** Lean beef including round roast/tip, sirloin, and lean ground

If you have any blood sugar-related diseases or disorders such as hyperglycemia, hypoglycemia, diabetes, or others, please CONSULT YOUR DOCTOR before following any of these food-combining guidelines.

❹ Eat Half Raw at All Meals

At least half of each meal you consume during your transformation plan should consist of raw fruit or vegetables, and this is why:

When foreign substances enter the body, the immune system sends white blood cells through the blood stream to "attack" these invaders. As a result, body parts become inflamed as white blood cells attempt to defend their precious tissues. While this reaction serves to protect the body, chronic (continued over time) inflammation is one of the leading causes of health decline, and plays a key role in the development conditions like Alzheimer's, arthritis, cancer, heart attack, lupus, psoriasis, and stroke—to name just a handful.

Two different studies in 2005 researched the effect eating a mostly raw vegetarian diet had on the body. The first, published in the Archive of Internal Medicine, found that subjects who ate a raw vegetarian diet showed significantly less inflammation in their bodies than the control group, who ate the Standard American Diet of cooked meat, processed carbohydrates, and salty fats. The second, published in the Journal of Nutrition found that those who followed a mostly raw food diet significantly lowered their LDL Cholesterol—the kind that is stored in your arteries' walls, causing the inflammation that leads to heart disease.

The **SUPERFOOD 6-WEEK TRANSFORMATION PLAN** recommends that all meals consist of at least 50% raw vegetables to fight the stress, strain , and unnecessary risks of excess inflammation. What a relief on your entire body!

❺ Indulge intelligently

On the seventh day, God said "Let there be chocolate!" At the end of every week, reward yourself with the divine taste of antioxidant-packed dark chocolate. Choose any of the following treats from the list to your right as a healthy indulgence.

And there was chocolate and antioxidants.
And it was good.

> ### DARK CHOCOLATE
>
> **Suggestions:**
> Green and Black's Organic Dark – 85% Cacao, Dagoba Eclipse – 87% Cacao, Scharffen Berger Extra Dark – 82% Cacao, Valrhona Noir Extra Amer – 85% Cacao, Sacred Chocolate.

TIPS AND TRICKS FOR A SUCCESSFUL PROGRAM

1. Be prepared

2. Move past mistakes

3. Be (somewhat) flexible

4. Drink Water, Naturally Flavored Water, and Herbal Teas

5. Write it down

6. Clean Cupboards, Clean Body

7. Snack Attack

8. Don't Shop Hungry

9. Eat before a party or dinner

NOTE: *The information contained in our guide and recipe book is not a substitute for regular health care. Before beginning this or any dietary program please consult with your physician regarding your health and nutrition.*

We understand that embarking on any lifestyle change can seem daunting, but with the **SUPERFOOD 6-WEEK TRANSFORMATION PLAN,** you are going to look and feel so good that any changes you make are WELL worth the effort! And NOTHING—not even cake or cookies—feels as good as feeling good!

We are confident that you will find that the more you follow this plan, the more you will WANT to follow this plan and continue on your quest to optimal health.

However, temptation is always a reality, and our fast paced lifestyles often pose a challenge to our healthy eating goals. The following tips and tricks will help your plan go as smoothly as possible.

① Be prepared

A well-laid path is easiest to follow. Most of this program requires homemade meals and snacks. The more of these dishes you have on hand during the week, the easier and more efficient it will be for you to follow the plan. When it's snacktime or lunchtime and you already know EXACTLY what you will be eating, you are far less likely to be tempted by something that doesn't fit into your program. It's a great idea to spend a weekend morning planning out your meals and snacks for the week; then purchase and prepare everything ahead of time. Freeze any dishes you plan on eating during the week; if you work outside of your home, bring your **TRANSFORMATION** meals on the road with you. **Half a day of preparation will set you up for a week of excellent eating.** Plus, you won't believe the time and money you'll save making your own foods!

TIPS AND TRICKS FOR A SUCCESSFUL PROGRAM

❷ Move past mistakes

Despite our best efforts, we humans are not perfect. If you accidentally munch a cupcake at your daughter's birthday party or eat a bag of chips as an emergency snack, don't give up on your plan. Forgive yourself and continue with the program as if those processed pieces never entered your system.

❸ Be (somewhat) flexible

On the same note as above, do not deny your body of its needs. This plan is specially formulated to meet and exceed daily nutrition requirements, but everybody and every body is different. If you find yourself famished or overly full, adjust your plan accordingly. Just be sure your body, not your head is driving the adjustment, and make sure that any extra portions fit with the plan's guidelines outlined in the **FIVE TO THRIVE KEYS TO SUCCESS.**

❹ Drink Water, Naturally Flavored Water, and Herbal Teas

While you will be drinking many of your meals in **NUTRIBLAST** form on this plan, it's very important not to forget to **drink plenty of water.** Staying hydrated will not only remind your stomach that you are satisfied, but also keep you focused, energetic, and less likely to stray from your goals. If you prefer flavored beverages, infuse your H_2O with mint, cucumber, lemon, or lime. Enjoy herbal and decaf green teas as much as you would like.

If you are a coffee drinker, limit yourself to one cup a day. Replace milk and cream with almond or hemp milk, and sugar with stevia extract.

Hold off on Happy Hour as best you can during your **SUPERFOOD 6-WEEK TRANSFORMATION PLAN.** Alcohol bogs down your digestive system and will hinder your transformation. A glass of wine here or there is okay, but for optimum results, ditch the booze for a spell.

⑤ Write it down

While the **NUTRIBULLET** provides the framework of this plan, it's up to you to fill in the specifics of what you consume. Keep track of meal and snack choices as well as portion sizes in the journal portion of this book. Record your meal and snack times as well to get a sense of your body's hunger cycle.

⑥ Clean Cupboards, Clean Body

Remove temptation by clearing your cupboards of processed, Standard American Diet foods. **Keep only clean, whole foods in your house.** Your body will thank you.

⑦ Snack Attack

It happens to the best of us. One minute we're waxing holistic about our new clean lifestyle, and the next we're clawing through our pantries to find something, ANYTHING sweet/salty/crunchy/all of the above (this is when **Tip #6** is on your side).

Fear not. There are plenty of **SUPERFOOD 6-WEEK TRANSFORMATION PLAN**-approved snacks that fit these criteria. When hunger strikes, turn to the following suggestions. Just be sure to cap your cravings at ONE SERVING.

Salty/Crunchy	Sweet

• Mary's Gone Crackers
 	
• Two Moms in the Raw Crackers
 	
• Edamame (1/2 c in shell with a sprinkle of salt)
 	
• Oil-free popcorn: Place ½ cup of popcorn in a large (3qts or bigger) microwave-safe glass bowl, cover and heat on high for 4-5 minutes. Stay nearby and remove as soon as popping slows down to prevent burning.
	• Frozen banana "ice cream": Freeze one banana unpeeled, in chunks. When a craving hits, blend the fruit in the NutriBullet short cup with a tsp of water or unsweetened almond/hemp milk until smooth. Add in walnuts and cacao nibs after blending for a special treat. It's amazing how similar the texture and flavor is to real banana ice cream— you'll wonder why you didn't switch to this version long ago!
	
	• Milk Shake: mix unsweetened almond milk, raw cacao powder, 6 to 7 cashews, a pinch of stevia, and goji berries with ice in the Short Cup. Pulse until mixture reaches an even milkshake consistency.
	
	• Raw vegan chocolate chip cookies:
	  – 2/3 c pitted dates
	  – 1/4 c cashews, almonds, or walnuts
	  – 1/4 c raw cacao nibs, chocolate chips, or 70% cacao bittersweet chocolate chips
	  – 1/4 tsp pure vanilla extract
	  Extract dates, nuts, and vanilla in the short cup until they reach a dough-like consistency. Mix in chocolate chips and form into bars, balls, or other shapes.
	
	• 1/2 oz raw cacao nibs with 1 tbs raisins

Sweet (continued)

- Power of Cacao: **NUTRIBLAST**
  - 1.5 cups of coconut water
  - 2 tbs honey
  - 45 blueberries (about 1 cup)
  - 15 raspberries
  - 3 tbs raw cacao nibs
  - 2 tbs raw almonds.

Place all ingredients in the **NUTRIBULLET** and extract.

❽ Don't Shop Hungry

Shopping while hungry will make you more tempted to purchase highly processed and overpriced convenience foods. Grocery shop after you've had a meal or snack, and remember that the less ingredients that "form" a food, the better that food is for your body!

❾ Eat before a party or dinner

While on the plan, you may find that social functions and restaurants do not serve foods that meet your requirements. Eat a **TRANSFORMATION** meal before heading to a dinner party, restaurant gathering, or any other social event. Order a green salad or snack on raw veggies during the gathering, and stay focused on the company you're with, not the cuisine.

Get ready to feel the best you have in years! Try not to approach this adventure in health as a strict 6-week commitment. You don't have to, because within a few days of following the plan, you will feel so good that you will be thrilled to eat this way, and nothing feels as good as feeling good!

A **NUTRIBLAST** is made up of 50% greens and 50% fruit. During your **SUPERFOOD 6-WEEK TRANSFORMATION PLAN,** we provide recipes as suggestions but you can always create your own blend by combining what you have in the fridge.

NUTRIBLAST

— MAX LINE —

Add water to MAX LINE

Add "boost"

50% fruit (as many varieties as possible!)

50% leafy greens
(2 cups = 1 serving)

NUTRIBLAST

LEAFY GREENS – 50%

Choose one from the following list of leafy greens or, mix and match! Fill the **Tall Cup** up to 50% with leafy greens. Work up to 2 full cups (2 handfuls) of leafy greens per 'Blast.

- ○ Collard Greens
- ○ Kale
- ○ Romaine
- ○ Spinach
- ○ Spring Greens
- ○ Swiss Chard

FRUITS – 50%

Choose as many fruits as you want to equal 50% of your **NUTRIBLAST.**

- ○ Apple
- ○ Avocado
- ○ Banana
- ○ Blackberry
- ○ Blueberry
- ○ Cantaloupe
- ○ Cranberry
- ○ Fig
- ○ Green Grapes
- ○ Guava
- ○ Honeydew
- ○ Kiwi
- ○ Mango
- ○ Nectarine
- ○ Orange
- ○ Papaya
- ○ Peach
- ○ Pear
- ○ Pineapple
- ○ Plum
- ○ Raspberries
- ○ Red Grapes
- ○ Strawberry
- ○ Watermelon

BOOSTS

The following ingredients are an important part of your **NUTRIBULLET NUTRIBLAST,** adding additional fiber and nutrition to every sip. Add 1/8 to ¼ cup to any 'Blast.

Nuts
- ○ Almonds
- ○ Cashews
- ○ Walnuts

Seeds
- ○ Chia Seeds
- ○ Flax Seeds
- ○ Hemp Seeds
- ○ Pumpkin Seeds
- ○ Sesame Seeds
- ○ Sunflower Seeds

Super Chargers
- ○ Goji Berries
- ○ Acai Berries

NOTE: *The information contained in our guide and recipe book is not a substitute for regular health care. Always consult your physician regarding health and nutrition.*

STAGE ①

Stage 1 takes place during **week 1** and **week 2** of your program. During this period, you will:

- Enjoy a Stage 1 **NUTRIBLAST** for daily breakfast
- Cut your animal product intake to 6 to 8 servings/week (meat, cheese, dairy)
- Cut your cooking oil intake to 1 tbs of olive oil/day

MEAL PLAN

① BREAKFAST:

Choose any Stage 1 **NUTRIBLAST** recipe on page 160, or create your own using any combination of fruits, greens, and boosts listed on page 153.

② MORNING SNACK:

Choose any Snack from the On-Track Snack List on page 150.

③ LUNCH:

Choose one dish from category A and one dish from category B.

A:	B:
• 1.5 cups Super Soup (pg 170)	• 2 cups Rawlicious Side Dish (pg 186)
• 1.5 cups Good Grains (pg 179)	• 2 cups Salad Greens of your choice
• 1 Wellness Wrap/ Sandwich (pg 175)	• 2 cups mixed raw veggies of your choice

4 AFTERNOON SNACK:

Choose any snack from the On-Track Snack List on page 150.

5 DINNER:

Choose one main dish from either category A or B and a side dish from category C.

A:	or	B:	with	C:
(4 oz Protein)		• 1.5 cups Vibrant Veggie Dinner of your choice (pg 192)		**(2 cups of)**
• **Poultry:** chicken breast, turkey breast				• Rawlicious Side Dish (pg 186)
• **Seafood:** salmon, halibut, tilapia, trout				• Salad Greens of your choice
• **Red Meat:** Lean beef including round roast/tip, sirloin, and lean ground				• Mixed raw veggies of your choice

6 DESSERT:

While we don't recommend daily desserts for the program, we do understand that everyone needs the occasional sweet treat. At the end of each week, enjoy one chocolate bar from our list on page 145. If you find you are desperate for treats during the week, check out our sweet section on page 150. Remember, this plan is for YOU and your health, so you are the best judge when it comes to indulging.

STAGE ②

Stage 2 takes place during **week 3** and **week 4** of your program. During this period, you will:
- Enjoy a stage 2 **NUTRIBLAST** for daily breakfast
- Include a small Green **NUTRIBLAST** as part of your daily lunch
- Cut your animal product intake to 4 to 6 servings/week
- Cut your cooking oil intake to 1 tbs of olive oil or coconut oil per day

MEAL PLAN

1 **BREAKFAST:**

Choose any Stage 2 **NUTRIBLAST** recipe on page 161, or create your own using any combination of fruits, greens, and boosts listed on page 153.

2 **MORNING SNACK:**

Choose any Snack from the On-Track Snack List on page 150.

3 **LUNCH:**

Enjoy one green **NUTRIBLAST** recipe on page 162 (Column A) with any dish from column B. Column C is optional.

A:	with	B:	or	C:
Short Cup **NUTRIBLAST** Recipes on (pg 161) 		• 1.5 cups Super Soup (pg 170) • 1.5 cups Good Grains (pg 179) • 1 Wellness Wrap/ Sandwich (pg 175)		**(2 cups of)** • Rawlicious Side Dish (pg 186) • Salad Greens of your choice • Mixed raw veggies of your choice

MEAL PLAN

4 **AFTERNOON SNACK:**

Choose any snack from the On-Track Snack List on page 150.

5 **DINNER:**

Choose one main dish from either category A or B and a side dish from category C.

A:		B:		C:
(4 oz Protein)	**or**		**with**	**(2 cups of)**

A:	B:	C:
(4 oz Protein) • **Poultry:** chicken breast, turkey breast • **Seafood:** salmon, halibut, tilapia, trout • **Red Meat:** Lean beef including round roast/tip, sirloin, and lean ground	• 1.5 cups Vibrant Veggie Dinner of your choice (pg 192) 	**(2 cups of)** • Rawlicious Side Dish (pg 186) • Salad Greens of your choice • Mixed raw veggies of your choice

6 **DESSERT:**

While we don't recommend daily desserts for the program, we do understand that everyone needs the occasional sweet treat. At the end of each week, enjoy one chocolate bar from our list on page 145. If you find you are desperate for treats during the week, check out our sweet section on page 150. Remember, this plan is for YOU and your health, so you are the best judge when it comes to indulging.

STAGE ③

Stage 3 takes place during the **week 5** and **week 6** of your program. During this period, you will:
- Enjoy a stage three **NUTRIBLAST** for daily breakfast
- Enjoy a large green **NUTRIBLAST** with lunch
- Eat 4 or less servings of animal products (meat, cheese, or dairy) per week
- Cut your cooking oil intake to 1/2 tbs of olive oil or coconut oil per day

MEAL PLAN

① BREAKFAST:

Choose any 'Blast recipe from the Stage 3 **NUTRIBLAST** menu on page 163, or create your own using any combination of fruits, greens, and boosts listed on page 153.

② MORNING SNACK:

Choose any Snack from the On-Track Snack List on page 150.

③ LUNCH:

Pair one large green **NUTRIBLAST** (pg 162) with one dish from category B.

A:	or	B:
Short Cup **NUTRIBLAST** Recipes on (pg 163) 		• 1.5 cups Super Soup (pg 170) • 1.5 cups Good Grains (pg 179) • 1 Wellness Wrap/ Sandwich (pg 175)

4 **AFTERNOON SNACK:**

Choose any snack from the On-Track Snack List on page 150.

5 **DINNER:**

Choose one main dish from either category A or B and a side dish from category C.

A:	or	**B:**	with	**C:**
(4 oz Protein)		• 1.5 cups Vibrant Veggie Dinner of your choice (pg 192)		**(2 cups of)**
• **Poultry:** chicken breast, turkey breast				• Rawlicious Side Dish (pg 186)
• **Seafood:** salmon, halibut, tilapia, trout				• Salad Greens of your choice
• **Red Meat:** Lean beef including round roast/tip, sirloin, and lean ground				• Mixed raw veggies of your choice

6 **DESSERT:**

While we don't recommend daily desserts for the program, we do understand that everyone needs the occasional sweet treat. At the end of each week, enjoy one chocolate bar from our list on page 145. If you find you are desperate for treats during the week, check out our sweet section on page 150. Remember, this plan is for YOU and your health, so you are the best judge when it comes to indulging.

STAGE ❶ NUTRIBLASTS

I. Immunity Mix
- 50% Spinach
- 50 % mixture of fruit:
  - 1 whole orange with rind
  - 1/2 of lemon with rind
  - 1/2 lime with rind
  - 1" chunk of ginger
  - Sprinkle of sea salt
  - 2 tbs organic raw honey

(Top with water to MAX LINE & extract)

II. Vita-Berry Blast
- 50% Spinach
- 50 % mixture of fruit:
  - 1/2 cup blueberries
  - 1 cup strawberries
  - 1 banana

(Top with water to MAX LINE & extract)

III. Protein Powerhouse
- 50% Spring Greens
- 50 % mixture of fruit:
  - 1/2 avocado
  - 1 cup raspberries
  - 1/2 cup mango
  - 10 cashews

(Top with water to MAX LINE & extract)

IV. Morning Glory
- 50% Spinach
- 50 % mixture of fruit:
  - 1/2 avocado
  - 1/2 cup mango
  - 1 tbs goji berries

(Top with water to MAX LINE & extract)

VI. Inflammation Elimination
- 50% Spring Greens
- 50 % mixture of fruit:
  - 1/4 lime with rind
  - 1/4 lemon with rind
  - 1/4 grapefruit with rind
  - 1 tbs flax seeds
  - 1/2 tsp tumeric

(Top with water to MAX LINE & extract)

OR Mix and Match
the following ingredients for your personalized blast:

Greens
Fill 50 % of your cup with:
- Spring Greens
- Spinach

Fruit
Mix and match the following to fill 50% of your cup:
- cup of pineapple, mango, honeydew, blackberries, strawberries, or raspberries
- apple
- avocado
- banana
- orange
- peach
- pear

Boosts
Top off your cup with the following amounts of these ingredients:
- 10 walnut halves
- 10 cashews
- 1 tbs goji berries
- 1/4 cup pumpkin seeds
- 1/4 cup hemp seeds

STAGE ② NUTRIBLASTS

I. Hormone Balancer (male)
- 50% Spring Greens
- 50 % mixture of fruit:
  - 1/4 small beet
  - 10 red seedless grapes
  - 2 small broccoli florets
  - 15 blueberries
  - 1/2 handful of pumpkin seeds
  - 1-2 tbs olive oil

(Top with water to MAX LINE & extract)

II. Hormone Balancer (female)
- 50% Butterhead Lettuce
- 50 % mixture of fruit:
  - 1/2 pitted peach
  - 1/2 cup blueberries
  - 3 Brazil nuts
  - 1 tsp maca powder

(Top with water to MAX LINE & extract)

III. Longevity Elixir
- 50% Romaine
- 50 % mixture of fruit:
  - 1/2 avocado
  - 1 cucumber
  - 1 cup cantaloupe
  - 12 cashews
  - 1 mint leaf

(Top with water to MAX LINE & extract)

IV. Fountain of Youth
- 50% Spinach
- 50 % mixture of fruit:
  - 1/2 cup red grapes with seeds
  - 1/2 cup raspberries
  - 10 almonds
  - 1 tsp maca powder

(Top with water to MAX LINE & extract)

V. Antioxidant Fusion
- 50% Butterhead Lettuce
- 50 % mixture of fruit:
  - 1/2 banana
  - 1/2 orange
  - 1/2 c pineapple
  - 10 almonds
  - 1 tbs cacao powder

(Top with water to MAX LINE & extract)

OR Mix and Match
the following ingredients for your personalized blast:

Greens
Fill 50 % of your cup with:
- Spring Greens
- Spinach

Fruit
Mix and match the following to fill 50% of your cup:
- blackberries, strawberries, or raspberries
- pineapple, mango, honeydew, or cantaloupe
- apple
- avocado
- banana
- orange
- peach, pitted
- pear
- cup of red grapes (with seeds)

Required Boosts
(at least one these)
Top off your cup with the following amounts of these ingredients:
- 10 walnut halves
- 10 almonds
- 12 cashews

Other Boosts
Top off your cup with the following amounts of these ingredients:
- 1 tsp maca powder
- 1 tbs sesame seeds
- 1 tbs chia seeds

161

STAGE ② GREEN DRINKS

☺ = **Good for beginners!**

Add one small green drink to your Stage 2 lunch. You can replace your raw salad with this drink, or you can enjoy both.

I. Jumping Ginger
- 1/2 carrot or 5 baby carrots
- handful of parsley
- 1 lemon, peeled
- 1/2 apple, cored and seeded
- 1-inch piece of ginger root
- 1/2 avocado

(Top with water to MAX LINE & extract)

☺ II. Banana Kale Bonanza
- 50% kale (about 5 leaves)
- 1/2 cup frozen mixed berries
- 1 banana
- 1 tbs hulled hemp seed

(Top with water to MAX LINE & extract)

☺ III. Avocado Watercress
- 1-inch piece ginger root
- handful watercress
- 1 stalk celery
- handful of spinach
- 1/2 pear
- 1/2 avocado
- 1 banana
- 1/2 cup frozen mixed berries

(Top with water to MAX LINE & extract)

☺ IV. Green Fever
- 50% spinach
- 1 banana
- 1 tomato

(Top with water to MAX LINE & extract)

V. Tomavocado
- 50% mixed greens
- 1/2 avocado
- 1 tomato
- 1 handful cilantro
- juice of 1/2 lime

(Top with water to MAX LINE & extract)

☺ VI. Mango Kale
- 50% kale
- 50% frozen mango

(Top with water to MAX LINE & extract)

OR Mix and Match
the following ingredients for your personalized blast:

Greens
Fill 50 % of your cup with one or more of the following:
- Spring Greens
- Spinach
- Kale
- Parsley
- Cliantro
- Watercress

Fruits and Vegetables
Mix and match the following to fill 50% of your cup:
- blackberries, strawberries, or raspberries
- mango
- apple
- avocado
- banana
- lemon or lime
- pear
- carrot
- stalk of celery
- tomato
- cucumber
- bell pepper

Other
Add these ingredients for a pop of flavor and health benefits:
- 1-inch piece of ginger root
- 1 tbs hemp seed
- pinch (1/2 tsp) chili powder

STAGE ③ NUTRIBLASTS

Stage 3 **NUTRIBLASTS** introduce some serious greens. The health benefits of these greens are so great, we hope you can handle the taste. Our saying is "the bitterer, the better," but if you can't enjoy these Stage 3 drinks as is, replace a portion of your greens with a milder green like spring greens or spinach. However, these dark greens are so good for you, do your best to include them!

I. Life Booster
- 50% Rinsed Kale
- 50 % mixture of fruit:
  - 1/2 pitted peach
  - 1/2 c strawberries
  - 1/2 avocado
  - 10 walnut halves
  - 1 tbs chia seeds
  - 1 tbs goji berries

(Top with water to MAX LINE & extract)

II. Banana Berry Vitality Blend
- 50% Rinsed Kale
- 50 % mixture of fruit:
  - 1/2 banana
  - 1/2 cup blueberries
  - 10 walnut halves
  - 1 tsp maca powder

(Top with water to MAX LINE & extract)

III. Power Booster
- 50% Swiss Chard
- 50 % mixture of fruit:
  - 1/2 banana
  - 1/2 pitted nectarine
  - 10 almonds
  - 1 tbs raw cacao powder

(Top with water to MAX LINE & extract)

IV. Digestive Health Elixir
- 50% Rinsed Swiss chard
- 50 % mixture of fruit:
  - 1/2 cup pineapple   – 3 Brazil nuts
  - 1/2 cup strawberries   – 1 tbs raw cacao powder

(Top with water to MAX LINE & extract)

V. Kaleacado Blast
- 50% Kale
- 50 % mixture of fruit:
  - 1/2 avocado   – 1/2 cup blueberries
  - 1/2 cup watermelon   – 12 cashews

(Top with water to MAX LINE & extract)

VI. Melon Blast
- 50% Kale
- 50 % mixture of fruit:
  - 1/2 cup raspberries   – 12 cashews
  - 1/2 cup cantaloupe   – 2 tbs goji berries

(Top with water to MAX LINE & extract)

VII. Power Booster
- 50% Swiss Chard
- 50 % mixture of fruit:
  - 1/2 banana   – 10 almonds
  - 1 cup raspberries   – 1 tbs cacao powder

(Top with water to MAX LINE & extract)

VIII. Swiss Mix
- 50% Swiss Chard
- 50 % mixture of fruit:
  - 1/2 banana   – 10 almonds
  - 1 cup raspberries   – 1 tbs cacao powder

(Top with water to MAX LINE & extract)

IX. Free Radical Fighter
- 50% Swiss Chard
- 50 % mixture of fruit:
  - 1 avocado   – 10 walnut halves
  - 1 small fig   – 1 tbs chia seeds
  - 1/2 cup blackberries   – 1 tbs cacao
  - 1/2 cup raspberries

(Top with water to MAX LINE & extract)

OR Mix and Match
the following ingredients for your personalized blast:

Greens
Fill 50 % of your cup with:
- Kale
- Swiss Chard
- Collard Greens

Fruits and Vegetables
Fill 50% of your cup with:
- blueberries, blackberries, raspberries, strawberries, grapes (with seeds), melon
- apple, banana, peach, plum, pear, avocado
- small fig, apricot, or nectarine

BOOSTS
Top off your cup with the following amounts of these ingredients; include one serving of nuts in every stage 3 Blast
- 10 walnut halves
- 12 cashews
- 10 almonds
- 3 Brazil Nuts
- 1 tbs goji berries
- 1 tbs pumpkin seeds
- 1 tbs chia seeds
- 1 tbs flax seed
- 1 tbs cacao
- 1 tbs sesame seed
- 1 tsp maca powder

ON TRACK SNACKS

1 Veggie Snacks

A. LifeBoost Dips and Veggies

Serve two of the vegetable servings listed below with two tablespoons of the dips listed below.

Veggies

- baby carrots or large carrots, peeled and sliced
- celery spears
- bell pepper, sliced
- cucumber, sliced
- cherry tomatoes
- cup sugar snap peas

LifeBoost Dips

Hummus (2 tbs/serving)

- 2 cloves of garlic
- 2 cups canned chick peas, rinsed and well drained
- 1 tsp sea salt
- 1/3 cup tahini
- Juice of 2 fresh lemons
- 1 tbsp extra virgin olive oil

Preparation:

1 Place all ingredients in NUTRIBULLET. Pulse with the Extractor Blade several times until well combined but still coarse. Adjust seasonings.

2 Transfer to serving bowl and serve or cover with plastic wrap.

LifeBoost Dips
Classic Guacamole (2 tbs/serving)
- 1 ripe avocado, peeled and pitted
- juice of 1 lime wedge
- 1 tbs cilantro
- 1/4 cup chopped red onion
- 1/2 clove garlic
- sea salt and pepper to taste

Preparation:

1 Place all ingredients in NUTRIBULLET. Pulse with the Extractor Blade several times until well combined but still coarse.

Baba Ganoush (2 tbs/serving)
- 1/2 large eggplant
- 1 tbs tahini
- 1 tbs lemon juice
- 1 cloves garlic
- pinch of chili powder
- 1 tbs olive oil
- salt to taste

Preparation:

1 Preheat oven to 400

2 Slice eggplant in half lengthwise and brush with olive oil. Place on foil lined sheet and bake for 45 mins until soft.

3 Allow eggplant to cool, then scoop out insides and combine in NUTRIBULLET using Extractor Blade with tahini, lemon juice, garlic, and chili powder, discarding the skins.

4 Drizzle in olive oil and blend again.

5 Add salt to taste.

Onion, Spinach, and Artichoke Dip (2 tbs/serving)

- 1/2 medium onion
- 1 clove garlic
- 3/4 cup fresh spinach
- 2/3 canned artichoke hearts, drained
- 1 cup nonfat plain Greek yogurt
- 1/2 tbsp chives
- Fresh cracked pepper to taste
- Sea salt to taste

Preparation:

1 Heat olive oil in a nonstick pan for one minute. Add onions and sauté until caramelized, about 5 to 10 minutes. Add garlic and sauté for 1 minute. Add spinach and cook for two minutes until just wilted. Allow to cool for 5 minutes.

2 Add spinach-onion mixture and artichoke hearts to the NUTRIBULLET. Pulse with extractor blade 1-3 times until minced. Add yogurt, chives, salt, and pepper. Pulse another 2 to 3 to times until vegetables and dairy are fully mixed.

3 Serve room temperature or chill in the refrigerator until eating.

B. Edamame

Enjoy 1 ½ cups of organic, non-gmo edamame in the pod or ¾ cups unshelled.

❷ Nutty Snacks

These snacks are tasty, satisfying and very portable. Enjoy!

A. Nutribars

One bar = one snack

Nut and Seed Bars

Making your own raw nut and seed bars is a really easy way to make delicious snacks that are perfect to take on the go.

Choose one of the following combinations, or mix and match to create your own:
• Cashew Apricot
• Walnut Date
• Almond Fig
• Pecan Prune
• Sesame Seed Apricot
• Pumpkin Seed Date

Preparation:

❶ Fill the Short Cup up to the max line with your favorite nuts.

❷ Use the pulsing technique to grind the nuts into a small, but still chunky consistency.

❸ Add in one fruit of your choice –
  • Apricot – cut off the tip and squeeze out the sticky center of 6 dried apricots into your pulsed nuts.
  • Date – cut off the tip and remove the pit, then squeeze out the sticky center or 4-6 dates into your pulsed nuts.
  • Figs – scoop out the meat of 2-3 ripe figs into your pulsed nuts.
  • Prune - cut off the tip and squeeze out the sticky center of 4 prunes into your pulsed nuts.

❹ Mix the ingredients together in the Short Cup with a spoon.

❺ Take handfuls of the mixture out of the cup and form into rectangular "bars".

❻ Wrap individual bars in wax paper or plastic wrap.

**Note – sometimes its easier to refine the "bar" shape shape once the mixture is already in wax paper or plastic. Use the counter top to flatten all four sides and ends.

Almond Cacao Goji Bar

- Almonds
- Figs
- Cacao Nibs
- Goji Berries
- Cacao Powder

Preparation:

1 Fill the Short Cup up to the max line with almonds. Use the pulsing technique to grind the nuts into a small, but still chunky consistency.

2 Place almond pieces in bowl.

3 Scoop out the meat of three ripe figs.

4 Add in cacao nibs (about 1/4 cup).

5 Add in goji berries (about 1/4 cup).

6 Add in 1 tbs of raw cacao powder.

7 Take handfuls of the mixture out of the cup and form into rectangular "bars."

8 Wrap individual bars in wax paper or plastic wrap.

**Note – As with the Nut and Seed Bars, sometimes its easier to refine the "bar" shape once the mixture is already in wax paper or plastic. Use the counter top to flatten all four sides and ends.

B. Trail Mix

Make your own energy mix with 14 cashews, almonds, pistachios, or walnut halves and 1 tbs unsweetened dried fruit.

C. Produce N' Nut Butter

Enjoy celery or carrot sticks, pear, apple, or banana with 1 tablespoon of cashew, almond, walnut, or pecan butter.

Enjoy for lunch at any stage.

Tomato Watermelon Gazpacho

- ¼ small seedless red watermelon (peeled cut into chunks)
- 2-3 large red beefsteak tomatoes (cut into chunks)
- 1 organic cucumber (cut into chunks)
- ¼ bunch parsley (cleaned and roughly chopped)
- ¼ bunch cilantro (cleaned and roughly chopped)
- ½ jalapeno (seeded and cut into chunks)
- ½ qt. tomato juice
- 4 shakes hot sauce
- 1 ½ Tbsp. Sherry vinegar
- Lime juice from ½ lime
- ½ tsp. Dijon mustard
- ½ diced avocado (optional)
- Salt and freshly ground pepper

Preparation:
Combine all the cut ingredients in a large glass bowl. Pour all the liquids over, and season with the salt and pepper. Allow mixture to marinate for at least a couple of hours, then add to NutriBullet Tall Cup and pulse with Extractor Blade until desired consistency is reached. Chill well before serving. Top with diced avocado if desired.

Pumpkin Soup

- 1 tbs olive oil
- 2 cups chopped onions
- 2 tsp whole wheat four
- 4 cups nonfat, reduced sodium vegetable stock
- 3 cups plain pumpkin purée
- ½ tsp minced garlic
- ½ can black beans
- ½ tsp ground cumin
- ¼ tsp salt
- ¼ tsp ground white pepper
- Dusting of grated nutmeg

Preparation:

1 Caramelize onion in olive oil in a skillet over medium heat.

2 Sprinkle in the flour and cook, stirring, 2 minutes or until mixture is slightly thickened. Add broth, whisking, then pumpkin, garlic, cumin, salt, and pepper. Bring the soup to a simmer, whisking occasionally and cook 15 minutes, stirring occasionally to prevent scorching. Add beans and cook 15 minutes, stirring occasionally to prevent scorching.

SUPER SOUPS

Ginger Pea & Brown Rice Soup

- 2 cups frozen peas (do not thaw)
- 1 1/2 cups low-sodium vegetable stock
- 1 tbs green onions
- 1 tsp miso paste
- 1 1/2 tsp ginger, coarsely chopped
- 10 basil leaves, coarsely chopped
- 1/2 cup cooked brown rice

Preparation:

❶ Heat peas in stock in a saucepan over medium heat. Cover and bring to a boil, about 10 minutes.

❷ Add all other ingredients except rice. Heat for one minute, then remove pot from heat.

❸ Allow to completely cool, then carefully pour mixture into NUTRIBULLET.*
Pulse with Extractor Blade until smooth. Re-heat as needed and pour over cooked brown rice in a bowl.

*NEVER BLEND WARM/HOT LIQUIDS IN THE NUTRIBULLET CUPS AS THIS MAY DAMAGE THE PIECES. ALWAYS BLEND COLD OR ROOM TEMPERATURE INGREDIENTS. ALLOW ALL COOKED INGREDIENTS TO COOL AT LEAST 30 MINUTES TO ROOM TEMPERATURE.

Tomato Soup

- 4 cups or 2 cans organic plum tomatoes
- 1 cup water or vegetable broth
- 1 onion
- 5 cloves garlic
- 2 medium sweet potatoes, peeled and chopped
- 1 to 2 handfuls of cashews
- salt and pepper to taste

Preparation:

❶ Place tomatoes and water/broth in a pot and bring to a boil, adding onion, sweet potato and garlic as they heat.

❷ Once the mixture boils, reduce heat to simmer for 10-15 minutes until potatoes are cooked through.

❸ Remove mixture from heat and allow to cool for 10-15 minutes. Add cooked mixture and cashews to NUTRIBULLET and puree with Extractor Blade until smooth.

*NEVER BLEND WARM/HOT LIQUIDS IN THE NUTRIBULLET CUPS AS THIS MAY DAMAGE THE PIECES. ALWAYS BLEND COLD OR ROOM TEMPERATURE INGREDIENTS. ALLOW ALL COOKED INGREDIENTS TO COOL AT LEAST 30 MINUTES TO ROOM TEMPERATURE.

Butternut Squash Soup

- 1 tbs olive oil
- 1 cup chopped white or yellow onion
- 1 medium apple, peeled, cored, seeded, and cut into chunks
- 2 ½ lbs butternut squash, peeled, seeded, and cut into chunks
- 4 cups vegetable broth
- 1 tbs curry powder
- 1 cinnamon stick or a pinch of ground cinnamon
- ¾ cup unsweetened coconut milk (optional)
- salt
- freshly ground pepper

Preparation:

❶ Cook onion, garlic, and apple in a pot in olive oil over medium heat until browned.

❷ Add all ingredients except coconut milk, salt, and pepper. Cover the pot and simmer mixture for 20 to 25 minutes until squash is tender.

❸ Remove from heat, discard cinnamon stick, and cool for at least 30 minutes until cool enough to blend.

❹ Add batches of squash mixture to NUTRIBULLET and puree with extractor blade until smooth.

❺ When ready to serve, return blended soup to pot, add coconut milk, and heat until hot. Add salt and pepper to taste.

> ***NEVER BLEND WARM/HOT LIQUIDS IN THE NUTRIBULLET CUPS AS THIS MAY DAMAGE THE PIECES. ALWAYS BLEND COLD OR ROOM TEMPERATURE INGREDIENTS. ALLOW ALL COOKED INGREDIENTS TO COOL AT LEAST 30 MINUTES TO ROOM TEMPERATURE.**

White Bean and Veggie (makes 6 servings)

- 1/2 tbs olive oil
- vegetable stock
- 1 cup sliced portabella or button mushrooms
- 2 carrots, diced
- 1 large onion, diced
- 2 celery stalks, diced
- 1 summer squash or zucchini, diced
- 4 garlic cloves, minced
- 1 tbs fresh basil
- 1 tsp dried thyme
- pinch cayenne pepper
- 1 bunch chopped kale, collards, or chard stems removed (and saved for NutriBlast)
- 2 cups of diced tomatoes
- 1 carton vegetable broth
- 2 cups canned white beans (cannellini, great northern, or navy)
- salt and ground pepper to taste

Preparation:

1 Heat oil in a large pot over medium heat. Add mushrooms, onion, carrots, celery, and zucchini/summer squash. Cook, stirring often, for 5 to 6 minutes. If veggies start sticking to the bottom of the pot, pour in just enough vegetable stock to keep them from sticking.

2 Add garlic, basil, thyme, and cayenne, and cook, stirring often, for 1 minute.

3 Add kale or chard and cook, stirring often, until the leaves have wilted.

4 Add tomatoes, broth, and beans, stirring to combine. If mixture seems thick, add 1 cup or so of water.

5 Bring to a simmer, reduce heat to medium-low, and continue to simmer for 20 minutes, stirring occasionally. Season with salt and pepper.

*NEVER BLEND WARM/HOT LIQUIDS IN THE NUTRIBULLET CUPS AS THIS MAY DAMAGE THE PIECES. ALWAYS BLEND COLD OR ROOM TEMPERATURE INGREDIENTS. ALLOW ALL COOKED INGREDIENTS TO COOL AT LEAST 30 MINUTES TO ROOM TEMPERATURE.

WELLNESS WRAPS AND SANDWICHES

Enjoy for lunch at any stage.

Quinoa Asparagus Wrap (makes 2 servings)

- 2 Whole Wheat Tortillas
- 1 cup of Cooked Quinoa
- 10 Steamed Asparagus Spears
- 1/4 cup diced tomato
- 1 handful of alfalfa or sunflower sprouts
- 1 lemon
- 1 TBS Veganaise (or Garlic Aioli)
- Pepper

Preparation:

1 Once cooked per quinoa's instructions, add Veganaise and juice of one lemon to one cup of cooked quinoa.

2 Lay out tortillas on a flat surface.

3 Divide and spread quinoa mixture onto the tortillas.

4 Add 5 steamed asparagus spears to each tortilla.

5 Add diced tomato and sprouts.

6 Roll up tortillas.

7 Enjoy.

Veggie Sandwich

- 2 Slices of Low Sodium Ezekiel Sprouted Bread
- Homemade Hummus (pg 165)
- Sliced Cucumber
- Sliced Tomato
- Sliced Red Onion (optional)
- 10 Leaves of Spinach (or other lettuce)

Preparation:

Build a yummy sandwich by layering the veggies on the hummus. Delish!

*Note – replace the hummus with any other LifeBoost dip for a tasty variation.

Eggplant Red Pepper Wrap

- 1 Whole Wheat Tortilla
- 2 TBS homemade baba ganoush* (pg 166)
- Handful of rinsed arugula
- 1/2 raw red pepper, thinly sliced into strips
- ¼ avocado
- Small segment of red onion, thinly sliced
- 1/4 lemon
- Unhulled sesame seeds
- Pepper

Preparation:

1 Lay out tortilla on a flat surface.

2 Spread baba ganoush onto the tortilla.

3 Layer arugula, red pepper, avocado, and onion onto the tortilla.

4 Squeeze the lemon wedge over the ingredients, remove any seeds that fall.

5 Season with sesame seeds and pepper.

6 Roll up tortilla.

7 Enjoy!

*Note – replace the baba ganoush with any other LifeBoost dip for a tasty variation.

Green Machine Wrap

- 1 Whole Wheat Tortilla
- 2 TBS homemade hummus (pg 165) or baba ganoush (pg 166)
- 1 medium kale or chard leaf
- ½ fresh green Serrano chili pepper, diced into small pieces
- sliced cucumber
- sliced tomato
- shredded carrot
- ¼ avocado
- 1 tbs all-natural salsa verde
- Unhulled sesame seeds
- Pepper

Preparation:

1 Lay out tortilla on a flat surface.

2 Spread hummus, baba ganoush, or green pea guacamole onto the tortilla.

3 Layer kale/chard, chili pepper, cucumber, tomato, carrot, and avocado onto the tortilla.

4 Spoon salsa over the ingredients.

5 Season with sesame seeds and pepper.

6 Roll up tortilla.

7 Enjoy.

Superfood Sushi (makes 1 6 to 8 piece roll)

This is a fun way to enjoy Nori—a nutritious sea vegetable—along with your more common raw veggies. Don't get discouraged if your rolls aren't perfect, the more rolls you make, the better your sushi skills will get. Plus, brown rice, veggies, and seaweed taste great no matter what shape they're in!

- 1/4 carrot, shredded
- 1/2 cup spinach or mixed greens
- 1/2 avocado, sliced into length-wise strips
- 1/4 cucumber, cut into matchstick pieces
- 1/4 carrot shredded or cut into matchsticks
- 2/3 cup sticky brown rice (technique follows)
- 1/4 cup alfalfa or sunflower sprouts
- 1 large sheet of nori seaweed
- raw, un-hulled sesame seeds
- sliced ginger and/or wasabi to garnish
- 1/4 cup Bragg's liquid aminos

Preparation:

1. Cook 3 cups of brown rice according to rice instructions, but add an extra cup of water to ensure sushi-worthy stickiness.
2. Lay out nori on a hard, flat surface.
3. Spread ¾ cup (or less) of your prepared sticky rice on the sheet in a thin layer, leaving at least ¼ inch of rice-free nori borders.
4. Line strips of veggies at the very edge of the nori, making sure they do not take up more than ¼ of the entire nori sheet.
5. Tightly roll your sushi, but not so tight as to break the nori.
6. Seal the edge of the roll by dipping your finger in water and running it across the open edge of the nori.
7. Slice with a sharp knife into 6 to 8 pieces.
8. Serve with ginger and/or wasabi and freely dip your sushi into Bragg's Liquid Aminos, a healthy soy sauce alternative.

Enjoy for lunch at any stage.

Wild Rice Lentil and Arugula Salad

- 2 cups cooked wild rice
- 2 cups cooked lentils
- 1/4 cup olive oil
- 1-2 cloves of garlic
- fresh thyme (optional)
- 2 lemons
- 2 cups organic arugula
- 2 tomatoes
- fresh sage (optional)

Preparation:

1 Prepare and cool 2 cups of your favorite wild rice blend.

2 Prepare and cool 2 cups of your favorite lentils.

3 Combine rice and lentils in a bowl.

4 Extract ¼ cup of olive oil, juice of 2 lemons, 1-2 cloves of garlic and fresh sage in the Short Cup until the ingredients are will blended.

5 Pour mixture over the rice and lentils.

6 Toss in 2 cups of fresh arugula.

7 Toss in 1 cup of chopped tomato.

8 Serve chilled or warm. If warm, serve rice and lentils on top of the arugula and pour "dressing" over top.

GOOD GRAIN SIDE DISHES

Quinoa "Stuffing"
- 2 cups cooked Quinoa
- 3 stalks celery
- 2 carrots
- pinch of sea salt
- dried cranberries

Preparation:

1 Prepare 2 cups of your favorite Quinoa and add to a bowl while still warm.

2 Chop 3 stalks of celery and add to bowl.

3 Chop 2 raw carrots and add to bowl.

4 Add ¼ cup (or more to taste) of dried cranberries and add to bowl.

5 Sprinkle with Himalayan Sea Salt and serve.

Alternative: To create more of a wintertime comfort food – add all ingredients to a casserole dish and bake at 350 for about 25 minutes.

Quinoa Tabouli
- 2 cups cooked quinoa
- 1/2 medium onion, minced
- 2 cloves garlic, press or chopped
- 2 cups fresh parsley
- 1 medium tomato, chopped
- 3 TBS extra virgin olive oil
- 1 TBS fresh lemon juice
- sea salt and pepper to taste

Preparation:

1 Add 2 cups of cooked quinoa to a bowl.

2 Place onion, garlic, parsley and tomato into the Short Cup and pulse until all of the ingredients are chopped/minced.

3 Pour this mixture over the quinoa.

4 Add olive oil, lemon juice and salt and pepper to the other ingredients and toss together.

5 Refrigerate.

Veggie Potato Salad

- 24 small red potatoes
- 2 ears of sweet corn
- 3 stalks celery
- 2 carrots
- 1 yellow pepper
- 1/4 cup of olive oil
- 1/4 cup of balsamic vinegar
- 1-2 cloves of garlic
- 2 sprigs of fresh thyme

Preparation:

1. Steam 24 small red potatoes and 2 ears of corn until soft.
2. Chill corn and cut kernels right off of the cobb into the bowl.
3. Chill and quarter the potatoes and place in bowl.
4. Chop 3 stalks of celery and add to bowl.
5. Chop 2 raw carrots and add to bowl.
6. Chop one yellow pepper and add to bowl.
7. In Short Cup combine ¼ cup of olive oil ¼ cup of balsamic vinegar, 1-2 cloves of garlic and 2 sprigs of fresh thyme. Blend until smooth.
8. Pour the mixture over the ingredients in the bowl and toss together.
9. Chill.

Mexican Casserole

- 2 cups brown rice
- 1 can organic black beans
- 1 clove of garlic (optional)
- 10 cherry tomatoes
- 1/4 of a small onion
- 4 sprigs of cilantro
- 1 jalapeño pepper
- 1/4 avocado

Preparation:

1 Prepare 2 cups of brown rice.

2 Heat 1 can of organic black beans with one minced garlic clove on the stove top.

3 Add 10 cherry tomatoes, ¼ of a small onion, 4 sprigs of cilantro, a jalapeno pepper (optional), and the juice of one lime to the Short Cup and pulse to make salsa.

4 In a casserole dish, spoon a layer brown rice on the bottom, then beans, then salsa.

5 Top with sliced avocado (or with a layer of guacamole see page 166).

6 Serve.

Note – avocado and guacamole turn brown very quickly when exposed to air. Add to casserole just before serving and squeeze lime on top to preserve their green color.

Chick Pea Summer Salad

While the chickpea is not a grain, it is a complex starch—which is what we want to incorporate in this list. Enjoy this deliciously beany recipe as you would the other Good Grain Side Dishes!

- 1 can organic chick peas
- 2 full sized tomatoes (or 20 cherry tomatoes)
- 5 stalks of celery
- 1/4 cup olive oil
- 1-2 cloves of garlic
- fresh thyme (optional)
- 2 lemons

Preparation:

1 Chop 5 stalks of celery add to bowl.

2 Chop 2 tomatoes (or quarter about 20 cherry tomatoes) add to bowl.

3 Drain one can of organic garbanzo beans and add to bowl.

4 Extract ¼ cup of olive oil, juice of 2 lemons, 1-2 cloves of garlic and fresh thyme in the Short Cup until the ingredients are well blended.

5 Pour the mixture over the ingredients in the bowl.

6 Sprinkle with Himalayan Sea Salt.

7 Serve or chill in refrigerator.

*Note – Other favorite veggies like raw red pepper or artichoke make delicious additions to this dish.

Chard and Pine Nut Risotto

This dish takes some time (and a couple of pots and pans) to prepare, but its decadent flavor and nutritious goodness are well worth the time and effort!

- 1 quart vegetable broth
- 5 cups water
- 1/4 cup pine nuts
- 2 tablespoons olive oil
- 1 cup finely chopped onion
- 2 cloves garlic, finely chopped
- 2 cups uncooked short-grain brown rice
- 4 cups coarsely chopped swiss chard leaves (about 1 bunch)
- Salt and pepper to taste

Preparation:

1 Mix broth and water together and simmer in a large pot. Leave simmering and cover.

2 Toast pine nuts in a dry skillet over medium-low heat, shaking frequently to brown evenly. Remove from heat when fragrant and brown. Transfer to a separate plate to cool.

3 Heat oil in a medium pot over medium heat. Add onion and garlic and cook, stirring occasionally, until softened, 4 to 5 minutes. Add uncooked rice and chard and stir gently, until rice is toasted and fragrant, and chard is wilted (roughly 4 to 5 minutes).

4 Add 1 cup of the broth-water mixture and cook, stirring constantly and adjusting heat if needed to maintain a simmer, until liquid is almost absorbed. Repeat process, adding about 1/2 cup of the broth-water mixture each time until rice is tender, about 35 minutes.

5 Season to taste, transfer to a medium bowl, and sprinkle with toasted pine nuts.

6 Enjoy!

Sweet Potato Oven Cakes (makes 4 servings)

Enjoy this baked version of the pan-fried potato pancake.

- 3 medium sweet potatoes, peeled and coarsely grated
- 1/2 onion
- 1/2 cup 100% applesauce (no sweeteners, thickeners, etc)
- 4 tbs whole wheat flour
- 1 tsp baking powder
- 1/2 tsp kosher salt
- 1/4 tsp black pepper

Preparation:

1. Preheat oven to 400 degrees.
2. Lightly grease a cookie sheet with olive or coconut oil.
3. Grate potatoes and onion into a large bowl. Add applesauce, flour, baking powder, salt, and pepper and mix thoroughly by hand.
4. Place rounded mounds of the mixture on cookie sheet (about 3" diameter).
5. Bake for 20 minutes, flip with a spatula, and bake on the other side for another 20 minutes or until golden brown.
6. Serve with more applesauce and grated horseradish.

Cucumber Salad

- 2 hot house or 4 regular cucumbers
- 1 small red onion
- 1/2 cup of Bragg's Apple Cider Vinegar
- 2 pinches of stevia
- 2 sprigs of thyme (optional)

Preparation:

1 Slice 2 organic hot house or 4 regular cucumbers (about ¼ inch thick) and add to a bowl.

2 Thinly slice a red onion add to bowl.

3 Add 1/2 cup of Bragg's Apple Cider Vinegar, 1 clove of garlic, 2 sprigs of fresh thyme (optional) and 2 pinches of stevia to the short cup and blend to smooth consistency.

4 Pour vinegar mixture over the ingredients in the bowl.

5 Toss and let sit overnight (it's good right away, but tastes even better when the ingredients hang out together for a while). Always toss a bit before serving.

Snappy Succotash (makes 4 servings)

- 1/2 cup of cooked edamame
- 1 cup of raw chopped green beans
- 1 cup of raw chopped cauliflower
- 1 cup of raw chopped tomato
- 1 cup of raw chopped red pepper
- 4 tbs olive oil
- juice of 2 lemons
- 4 tbs of balsamic vinegar
- 1-2 cloves of garlic
- 2 sprigs of fresh thyme (optional)

Preparation:

1. Chop all vegetables and add to a large salad bowl.
2. Extract ¼ cup of olive oil, juice of 2 lemons, 1-2 cloves of garlic, ¼ cup of balsamic vinegar and fresh thyme in the Short Cup until the ingredients are will blended.
3. Pour the dressing mixture onto the veggies and toss together.
4. Serve or chill.

(MOSTLY) RAWLICIOUS SIDE SALADS

Raw Slaw

- 1 cup shredded and chopped carrots
- 1 cup shredded and chopped red cabbage

- 2 cups shredded and chopped green cabbage

- 1 tsp. celery seed

- 1 tsp. garlic powder

- 2-3 tbs fresh pepper
- 2 Tbsp. maple syrup

- 3 heaping tbsp. Veganaise
- 1/4 cup lemon juice to taste

Preparation:

1 Add first 6 ingredients to a large salad bowl.

2 Add maple syrup or agave, Veganaise and lemon to the Short Cup Blend until all of the ingredients are combined well.

3 Pour the mixture over the salad ingredients and toss together.

4 Chill.

Veggie Cobb

- 6 cups of fresh chopped romaine lettuce
- 1 cup mandarin orange slices (if canned, NO SYRUP)
- 1/3 cup sliced black olives (optional)
- 1/2 cup chopped sweet onion
- 1 avocado, chopped
- 1 cup cherry tomatoes, halved
- ½ cup chilled kidney beans, drained
- 1 cup hearts of palm (diced)
- ¼ cup of olive oil
- juice of 2 lemons
- 1/8 cup of balsamic vinegar
- 1-2 cloves of garlic
- 2 sprigs of fresh basil (optional)

Preparation:

1 Add the first 8 ingredients to a large salad bowl.

2 Add olive oil, lemon, balsamic vinegar, garlic and basil to the Short Cup and blend until smooth.

3 Pour dressing over the salad.

4 Devour!!

Tomacavo-Basil Layered Salad

Salad:

- 1/2 beefsteak tomato
- 1/2 avocado
- 8-12 large fresh basil leaves

Dressing:

- 1 tbs hummus (pg 165)
- 2 tbs balsamic vinegar

Preparation:

1 Slice tomato into ¼-inch thick slices.

2 Slice avocado into ¼-inch thick slices.

3 Tear off, rinse and dry basil.

4 Layer tomato, basil, and avocado to make a striped presentation.

5 Add hummus and vinegar to the Short Cup and extract until smooth.

6 Pour over salad just before serving.

Preparation:

- Serve the salad over a bed of fresh arugula for extra greens.
- Substitute cilantro for basil and red wine vinegar for balsamic for a different flavor combination.

Sprout and About (serves 4)

- 1 shallot, peeled and thinly sliced
- 1 small fennel bulb, thinly sliced
- 1 1/2 tsp raw agave nectar, or raw honey
- 4 tbs apple cider vinegar
- 1 tsp ground mustard seed
- 3 tbs olive oil
- Salt and pepper to taste
- 1 pint of cherry or grape tomatoes, halved
- 2 cups lentil sprouts
- 2 cups alfalfa sprouts
- 3/4 pound baby spinach or mâche

Preparation:

1 Soak shallot in ice water for 30 minutes.

2 Add vinegar, ground mustard, agave, and olive oil to Short Cup and extract until smooth.

3 Dry shallot and toss with tomatoes, fennel, sprouts, and spinach/mâche.

4 Pour dressing over, toss, and top with salt and fresh ground pepper.

5 Enjoy!

DINNERS

Pick one from category A or B and serve with category C.

A:	or	B:	with	C:
(4 oz Protein)		• 1.5 cups Vibrant Veggie Dinner of your choice (pg 192)		**(2 cups of)**
• **Poultry:** chicken breast, turkey breast				• Rawlicious Side Dish (pg 186)
• **Seafood:** salmon, halibut, tilapia, trout				• Salad Greens of your choice
• **Red Meat:** Lean beef including round roast/tip, sirloin, and lean ground				• Mixed raw veggies of your choice

❶ Protein Dinners

Enjoy Four ounces of lean protein with 2 cups of the Rawlicious Salad or raw vegetable mixture of your choice.

Meat/fish can be grilled, baked, or pan-seared—no frying or breading. Garnish with fresh lemon juice, balsamic vinegar, Bragg's liquid aminos, or Cobb Salad balsamic vinaigrette (pg 189). Feel free to experiment and create your own sauces – just be sure they follow the plan's guidelines.

❷ Vibrant Vegetarian Dinners

Enjoy 1½ cups of vibrant veggie dish w/2 cups of the Rawlicious Salad or raw vegetable mixture of your choice.

Lentil Stew

- 2 cups chopped carrots
- 2 cups chopped celery
- 2 cups zucchini
- 1 cup chopped onion
- 1 cup chopped cauliflower
- 1 cup chopped tomato
- 2 cups cooked lentils
- 1/2 - 1 TBS extra virgin olive oil
- 4 cups of veggie broth.
- Salt and Pepper to taste

Preparation:

❶ Add olive oil to the bottom of a large stock pot and heat over medium heat.

❷ Add carrots, celery and onion and sauté until a bit tender.

❸ Add cauliflower and sauté until a bit tender.

❹ Add lentils.

❺ Add veggie broth.

❻ Bring to a boil then reduce heat back down to low.

❼ Add in tomatoes and heat for 20 minutes.

❽ Salt and pepper to taste.

Note – add your favorite seasonings to taste. Serve with a slice of Ezekiel bread or pour over ½ cup of brown rice, quinoa, or whole wheat pasta.

Pasta Fagioli

- 1 cup diced celery
- 1 cup chopped green beans
- 2 carrots, sliced thin
- 2 ripe plum tomatoes peeled & chopped
- 2 Tbsp organic tomato paste, or 1/2 cup tomato sauce
- 1 cup cooked kidney beans or cannellini beans
- 8 oz cooked whole wheat or brown rice pasta
- 1 Tbsp olive oil
- 1 clove garlic, peeled & minced
- 1/2 tsp ground fennel seed
- 1/2 tsp ground coriander seed
- 1 tsp dried basil OR 1 Tbsp
- Salt and pepper to taste
- 2 Tbsp minced fresh basil or Italian parsley for garnish
- 4 cups veggie broth

Preparation:

1. Cook pasta according to instructions.
2. Heat the oil on low in a 6 - 8 quart pan.
3. Add the minced garlic to the oil and heat on medium low until lightly browned.
4. Add in carrots, celery, green beans, & chopped fresh tomatoes, and sauté 5 minutes on med/high heat.
5. Add the herbs and spices, sauté briefly.
6. Add the veggie broth.
7. Drain and rinse the kidney beans, then add to pot.
8. Add tomato paste or tomato sauce, cover and simmer until veggies are tender.
9. Add the pasta, salt and pepper to taste.
10. Cook for 10 more minutes, adding more water or stock as desired.
11. Serve garnished with fresh basil or Italian parsley.

Veggie Chili

- 3 cloves of garlic
- 4 tomatoes
- 1 cups chopped carrots
- 1 cups chopped celery
- 1 cups zucchini
- 1 cup chopped onion
- 1 cup of chopped bell pepper
- 1 chopped jalepeno pepper (optional)
- 1 can of kidney beans
- 1 can of pinto beans
- 1 can of black beans
- 2 tbs oregano
- 1/2 cup veggie broth
- 1/2 tbsp olive oil

Preparation:

1 Place garlic and tomatoes in the Tall Cup and pulse until you've achieved a diced consistency.

2 Add olive oil to the bottom of a large stock pot and heat over medium.

3 Add in onion, peppers, carrots, celery and zucchini into the pot and cook until tender.

4 Add in extracted tomato mixture, beans, broth and oregano and heat over medium heat while stirring all of the ingredients together for about 10 minutes.

5 Turn heat to low and heat for about an hour – stirring on occasion.

6 Serve.

Butter Bean and Broccolini Soba Noodles

- 1 bundle of 100% whole buckwheat soba noodles
- 1/2 tbs coconut or olive oil
- 3-6 stalks of broccolini, depending on size
- pinch of cayenne pepper
- black pepper
- salt
- 10 red or yellow grape tomatoes, halved
- 1/2 cup butter beans, rinsed and drained (canned butter beans)
- 1 tbs rice vinegar
- 1 tsp oregano
- 1 tsp basil
- Balsamic or apple cider vinegar, for drizzling

Preparation:

1 Heat a large pot of salted water to a boil. Add soba noodles and cook as package directions indicate, then drain and rinse well. Set noodles aside.

2 Steam broccolini until it turns bright green (about two minutes) and set aside.

3 In a nonstick pan, heat olive/coconut oil. Stir in quartered cherry tomatoes, cayenne, salt, and pepper. Add steamed broccolini and let cook for 1-2 minutes so all the pan ingredients get a little caramelized and soften up. Once tomatoes are softened, add 1/2 cup of butter beans. Stir everything together and remove to a bowl.

4 In the still-hot pan, add 1-2 tbs of rice vinegar. Add cooked soba noodles to the hot pan, seasoning with a pinch each of salt, basil, and oregano. Toss to coat the pasta. Once the pasta is coated and is heated through, add back the broccolini, beans, and tomatoes. Taste and season with more salt or pepper if needed.

5 Plate, and drizzle with balsamic or cider vinegar if desired.

Protein Pot

- 1/2 cup uncooked chickpeas
- 1/2 cup uncooked lentils
- 1 cup uncooked speltberries, quinoa, bulgar wheat, or whole wheat pasta
- 1/2 tbs olive or coconut oil for sautéing
- 1/2 red onion, chopped
- 3-4 cloves of garlic, minced
- 1 red bell pepper, chopped
- 1 large tomato, chopped
- 3 cups spinach or kale, roughly chopped
- 1/2 cup fresh parsley or cilantro, minced
- 2 tbs tahini
- 2 lemon wedges

Preparation:

1 Cook chickpeas and speltberries (or grain of choice) according to package directions. Drain and set aside.

2 In a large skillet over low-medium heat, add your olive oil and sauté the chopped onion and minced garlic for a few minutes, being careful not to burn. Now add in the chopped red pepper and tomato and sauté for another 7-8 minutes.

3 Stir in the chopped kale or spinach and sauté for another few minutes, just until tender. Stir in the tahini, the cooked & drained grains and chickpeas, and simmer on low for another few minutes. Remove from heat and stir in the minced parsley/cilantro. Season with salt and pepper to taste and garnish with lemon wedges and zest. Makes 6 cups.

Nut Loaf

- 8 oz chopped mixed nuts
- 1 onion, chopped
- 1 clove of garlic, minced
- 1 red pepper, chopped
- 1/2 cup broccoli, finely chopped
- 1 stick of celery, chopped
- 1 grated carrot
- 1 cup mushrooms, finely chopped
- 2 oz sprouted wheat breadcrumbs** (recipe to follow)
- 1 oz regular, unbleached whole wheat flour
- 5 oz vegetable stock
- 1 tsp thyme
- 1 tsp oregano
- salt and pepper to taste
- 1 TBSP olive or coconut oil

Preparation:

1 Preheat oven to 375 °F.

2 Heat oil in a pan and sauté the onion for a few minutes.

3 Add pepper, celery and mushrooms and sauté for 2 more minutes.

4 Add the garlic and grated carrot and fry for one more minute.

5 Remove from the heat, add flour and stir.

6 Add vegetable stock, nuts, breadcrumbs, thyme, oregano, and a little salt and pepper.

7 Grease the inside of a loaf tin with olive oil or olive oil spray. Put the mixture into the tin, pressing it down with a spoon.

8 Bake for around 35 minutes.

9 Slice into ½-thick slices and serve with a large raw vegetable salad.

**Sprouted Wheat breadcrumbs: Toast two slices of Eziekiel or other sprouted wheat bread to medium brown. Place in Short Cup and pulse 2-3 times in NutriBullet until just broken up.

Curried Fava Beans (makes 2 servings)

- 1 large yellow onion cut in pieces
- 2 garlic cloves, peeled
- 1-inch piece of fresh ginger root, peeled and chopped
- 1 tbs olive oil
- 1 tbs curry powder
- 1/2 tsp ground cardamom
- 1/2 tsp ground cinnamon
- 1/2 tsp dry mustard
- 1/4 tsp cayenne
- 1/4 tsp ground allspice
- 1/4 tsp turmeric
- 1/4 tsp paprika
- 1 cup water
- 1 ½ cups canned fava beans (substitute 1 ¼ c cooked lentils if unavailable)
- 2 medium sized carrots, halved lengthwise and sliced into thin semicircles
- 3/4 cups green peas
- 1/2 tomato, diced
- 3/4 c light coconut milk
- salt and freshly ground pepper to taste

Preparation:

1 Pulse the onion, garlic, and ginger in the NutriBullet until smooth.

2 Heat olive oil in a large saucepan over low heat.

3 Add the onion, garlic, and ginger puree, cover, and cook about five minutes to mellow the flavor, stirring occasionally.

4 Stir in the spices, then add carrots and water.

5 Cook, covered, for 20-30 minutes, until carrots are tender.

6 Add the fava beans, tomatoes peas, coconut milk, coconut, and salt and pepper to taste.

7 Simmer another 10 minutes.

8 Serve alone or over ½ cup of brown rice, quinoa, or bulgar wheat.

Portabella Burger (makes 4 servings)

- 4 medium portabella mushrooms, stems removed
- 1 medium onion, cut into 1/2 inch slices
- 2 tbsp olive oil
- 3/4 tsp salt, divided
- 1/2 teaspoon ground black pepper, divided
- 1 avocado, sliced
- 1/2 tsp minced garlic
- 4 whole wheat buns or whole wheat English Muffins, lightly toasted
- 4 jarred roasted red peppers

Preparation:

1 Brush mushrooms and onion slices with oil; sprinkle with 1/2 teaspoon of the salt and 1/4 teaspoon of the pepper.

2 Heat large skillet or grill pan over medium heat until hot. Add mushrooms; cook until tender, 8 to 10 minutes, turning once. Transfer mushrooms to plate, cavity side up; cover to keep warm.

3 In same skillet, cook onion slices until golden, about 8 minutes, turning occasionally.

4 Meanwhile, combine ½ avocado, garlic and remaining 1/4 teaspoon each salt and pepper; mash until smooth. You can also skip this step and use any pre-made guacamole or sweet pea guacamole from the On-Track Snack Dip list (pg 166).

5 Spoon onions and roasted peppers into mushroom cavities, divided equally. Spread smooth Avocado mixture/guacamole/green pea guacamole on bottom of each bun/English Muffin; top each with stuffed mushrooms.

6 Top with remaining sliced avocado. Cover with tops of buns/English Muffins.

7 Serve with a large raw vegetable salad.

Sources

Anderson, Richard A. "Chromium and Polyphenols from Cinnamon Improve Insulin Sensitivity." The Summer Meeting of the Nutrition Society. Irish Section. University of Ulster, Coleraine. 16-19 July, 2007. Lecture.

Antoniou, L.D., and R.J. Shalhoub. "Zinc-Induced Enhancement of Lymphocyte Function and Viability in Chronic Uremia." *Nephron* . 40.1 (1985): 13-21. Web. <http://content.karger.com/ProdukteDB/produkte.asp?Aktion=ShowAbstractB

Al Badir, Nawal. "Improvement Effect of Tomato Seeds and Vitamin C on Potassium Bromate Induced Renal Injury in Rats." *Journal of American Science* . 7.9 (2011): 549-555. Web. <http://www.jofamericanscience.org/journals/am- sci/am0709/070_6843am0709_549_555.pdf>.

Al-Suhaumi, Ebtesam A., Noorah A. Al-Riziza, et al. "Physiological and Therapeutic Roles of Ginger and Turmeric on Endocrine Functions." *American Journal of Chinese Medicine.* 39.2 (2011): 215-231. Web. <http://www.worldscinet.com/ajcm/39/3902/S0192415X11008762.html>.

Arnaud, M J. "Mild dehydration: a risk factor of constipation?." *European Journal of Clinical Nutrition.* 57.2 (2003): n. page. Web. <http://www.nature.com/ejcn/journal/v57/n2s/full/1601907a.html>.

"B vitamins slow brain atrophy in people with memory problems." *University of Oxford.* University of Oxford, 9/9/2010. <http://www.ox.ac.uk/media/news_stories

Balch, Phyllis A. *Prescription for Dietary Wellness.* 2nd edition. New York: Avery/Penguin Group, 2003. Print.

Balch, Phyllis A. *Prescription for Nutritional Healing.* Fifth edition. New York: Avery/Penguin Group, 2010. Print.

Behl, C, J Davis, et al. "Vitamin E protects nerve cells from
amyloid beta protein toxicity.." *Biochemical and Biophysical
Research Communications.* 186.2 (1992): 944-950. Web. <http://ukpmc.ac.uk/abstract/
MED/1497677/reload=0;jsessionid=ixiK0Ceo236Gsmle3w1v.4>.

Bresson, Jean-Louis, Albert Flynn, et al. "Scientific Opinion on the substantiation of
health claims related to vitamin A and cell differentiation (ID 14), function of immune
system (ID 14), maintenance of skin and mucous membranes (ID 15, maintenance
of vision (ID 16), maintenance of bone (ID 13, 17), maintenance teeth (ID 13, 17),
maintenance of hair (ID 17), maintenance of nails (ID 17), metabolism of iron (ID 206),
and protection of DNA, proteins and lipids from oxidative damage (ID 209) pursuant
to Article 13(1) of Regulation (EC) No 1924/2006." *European Food Safety Association
Journal.* 7.9 (2009): 1-25.
<http://www.efsa.europa.eu/en/efsajournal/pub/1221.htm>.

Cohen, Jennifer H., Alan R. Kristal, et al. "Fruit and Vegetable Intakes and Prostate
Cancer Risk." *Journal of the National Cancer Institute* . 92.1 (2000): 61-68. Web.
<http://jnci.oxfordjournals.org/content/92/1/61.long

Combs, Gerald F. "Current Evidence and Research Needs to Support a Health Claim
Selenium and Cancer Prevention." *Journal of Nutrition* . 135.2 (2005): 343-347. Web.
<http://www.ncbi.nlm.nih.gov/pubmed/15671240>.

David, J.A., W.C. Cyni, et al. "Effect of a Low–Glycemic Index or
a High–Cereal Fiber Diet on Type 2 Diabetes." *Journal of American Medicine.* 300.23
(2008): 2742. Web. <http://jama.ama-assn.org/content/300/23/2742.short>.

Eagleman, David. Incognito: *The Secret Lives of the Brain.* First Edition. New York:
Pantheon, 2011. 1-2. eBook.
<http://www.amazon.com/Incognito-Secret-Lives-Brain-ebook/dp/B004J4WK9W>.

Eberhardt, Marian V., Chang Yong Lee, and Rui Hai Liu.
"Nutrition: Antioxidant activity of fresh apples." *Nature.* 405. (2000): 903-904. Print.
<http://www.nature.com/nature/journal/v405/n6789/abs/405903b0.html>.

Ernst, E., and M.H. Pittler. "Efficacy of ginger for nausea and
vomiting: a systematic review of randomized clinical trials." *British Journal of Anaesthesia.*
84.3 (2000): 367-371.
Web. <http://bja.oxfordjournals.org/content/84/3/367>.

Ershler, William B. "The Influence of an Aging Immune System on Cancer Incidence
and Progression." *Journal of Gerentology: Biological Sciences.* 48.1 (1993): B3-B7. Web. 3
May. 2012. <http://geronj.oxfordjournals.org/content/48/1/B3.full.pdf>.

Facchinetti, Fabio, Paola Borella, et al. "Oral Magnesium Successfully Relieces
Premenstrual Mood Changes." *Obstetrics & Gynecology* . 78.2 (1991): 177-181.
Web. <http://www.ncbi.nlm.nih.gov/pubmed/2067759>.

"Folic Acid." *www.cancer.org.* American Cancer Society, n.d. Web.
<http://www.cancer.org/Treatment/TreatmentsandSideEffects/Complementary acid>.

Funk, Janet L., and Janice N. Oyarzo. "Turmeric Extracts Containing Curcuminoids
Prevent Experimental Rheumatoid Arthritis." *Journal of Natural Products.* 69.3 (2006): 351-
355. Web. <http://www.ncbi.nlm.nih.gov/pmc/articles/PMC2533857/>.

Gao, K, SM Henning, et al. "The citrus flavonoid naringenin stimulates DNA repair
prostate cancer cells.." *Journal of Nutritional Biochemistry* . 17.2 (2006): 89-95.
Web. <http://www.ncbi.nlm.nih.gov/pubmed/16111881>.

Ghanbari, Zinat, Fedieh Haghollahi, et al. "Effects of Calcium Supplement Therapy i Women with Premenstrual Syndrome." *Taiwanese Journal of Obstetrics and Gynecology* . 48.2 (2009): 124-129. Web.

Ghanbarali, Raeis Jalali. "Impact of oral zinc therapy on the level of sex hormones in male patients on hemodialysis ." *Renal Failure* . 32.4 (2010): 417-419. Web. <http://informahealthcare.com/doi/pdf/10.3109/08860221003706958>.

Guarrera, Simonetta, and Carlotta Sacerdote. "Expression of DNA repair and metabo genes in response to a flavonoid-rich diet." *British Journal of Nutrition* . 98. (2007): 525-534. Web. <http://www.ncbi.nlm.nih.gov/pubmed/17445347>.

Guyonnet, D, A Schlumberger, et al. "Fermented milk containing Bifidobacterium lactis DN- 173 010 improves gastrointestinal well-being and digestive symptoms in women reporting minor digestive symptoms: a randomised, double-blind, parallel, controlled study.." *British Journal of Nutrition.* 102.11 (2009): 1654-62. Web. <http://www.ncbi.nlm.nih.gov/pubmed/19622191>.

Haverstein, Bent H. "The biochemistry and medicalsignificance of the flavonoids." *Pharmacology & Theraputics.* 96.2-3 (2002): 67-202. Web. <http://www.sciencedirect. com/science/article/pii/S016372580200298X>.

Health Effects of Omega-3 Fatty Acids on Cardiovascular Risk Factors and Intermediate Markers of Cardiovascular Disease, Structured Abstract. March 2004. Agency for Healthcare Research and Quality, Rockville, MD. http://www.ahrq.gov/clinic/tp/o3cardrisktp.htm

Hillman, Lybus, and Sue Peters. "Differing effects of pectin, cellulose and lignin on stool pH, transit time and weight ." *British Journal of Nutrition.* 50.2 (1983): 189-195. Web. <http://journals.cambridge.org/action/displayAbstract?from Page=online&aid=849596>.

"Increasing Daily Servings of Green Leafy Vegetables and Fruits
Rich in Vitamin C Reduces Risk of Heart Disease." Harvard School of Public Health. Boston, June 18, 2001. Press Release.

Irshad, Saba, Muneeba Butt, et al. "In-Vitro antibacterial activity
of Aloe Barbadensis Miller (Aloe Vera)." *International Research Journal of Pharmeceuticals.* 01.2 (2011): 60-65. Print. <http://www.scientific-journals.co.uk/web_documents/irjp_09_in-vitro_ antibacterial_activity_of_aloe_barbadensis_miller__aloevera.pdf>.

Jenny, M, E Santer, et al. "Cacao extracts suppress tryptophan
degradation of mitogen-stimulated peripheral blood mononuclear cells." *Journal of Ethnopharmacology.* 122. (2009): 161-267. Web. <http://www.journals.elsevier.com/journal-of-ethnopharmacology/

Jonkers, D., E. van der Broek, et al. "Antibacterial effect of garlic and omeprazole on
Helicobacter pylori." *Journal of Antimicrobial Chemotherapy* . 43.6 (1999): 837-839. Web. <http://jac.oxfordjournals.org/content/43/6/837.full>.

Jouris, Kelly B., Jennifer L. MacDaniel, et al. "The effect of omega-3 fatty acid
supplementation on the inflammatory response to eccentric strength exercise." *Journal of Sports Science and Medicine* . 10. (2011): 432-438. Web. 30 Mar. 2012. <http://www.jssm.org>.

Kaczmarczyk, MM, MJ Miller, et al. "The health benefits of
dietary fiber: Beyond the usual suspects of type 2 diabetes mellitus, cardiovascular disease and colon cancer.." *Metabolism.* (2012): n. page. Web. <http://www.ncbi.nlm.nih.gov/ pubmed/22401879>.

Kohlmeier, Martin, Jörg Saupe, et al. "Bone health of adult hemodialysis patients is
related to vitamin K status." *Kidney International.* 51. (1997): 1218-1221. Web. <http://www. nature.com/ki/journal/v51/n4/abs/ki1997166a.html>.

Lawrence, Rubina, and Priyanka Tripathi. "Isolation, Purification
    and Evaluation of Antibacterial Agents from Aloe vera." *Brazilian Journal of Microbiology.*
    40.4 (2009): n. page. Web. <http://www.scielo.br/scielo.php?script=sci_arttext&pid
    =S1517-83822009000400023>.

Lim, Giselle, Frédéric Calon, et al. "A Diet Enriched with the
    Omega-3 Fatty Acid Docosahexaenoic Acid Reduces Amyloid Burden in an Aged Alzheimer
    Mouse Model." *Journal of Neuroscience.* 25.12 (2005): 3032-3040. Web. <http://www.
    neuro.cjb.net/content/25/12/3032.full>.

"Linus Pauling Institute at Oregon State University." *Zinc.* Oregon
    State University, n.d. Web. <http://lpi.oregonstate.edu/infocenter/minerals/zinc/>.

Loening-Bauke, Vera, Erasmo Miele, et al. "Fiber (Glucomannan)
    Is Beneficial in the Treatment of Childhood Constipation." *Pediatrics.* 113.3 (2004): 259-
    264. Web. <http://pediatrics.aappublications.org/content/113/3/e259.short>.

"Macular Degeneration." *University of Maryland Medical Center.* University of
    Maryland Medical Center, n.d. Web. <http://www.umm.edu/altmed/articles/macular-

Makover, Michael E., MD, and David Zieve, MD, eds.
"Fibromyalgia: In-Depth Report." The New York Times. The New York Times & A.D.A.M,
14/02/2011. Web. 21 Jun 2012.http://health.nytimes.com/health/guides/disease/fibromyalgia/
overview.html

McBride, Judy. United States. United States Department of Agriculture. High-ORAC
    Foods May Slow Aging. 1999. Web. <http://www.ars.usda.gov/is/pr/1999/990208.htm>.

Morganti, P. "New chitin complexes and their anti-aging activity from inside out."
    Journal of Nutrition, Health, and Aging. 16.3 (2012): 242-245.
    Web. 10 Apr. 2012. <http://www.ncbi.nlm.nih.gov/pubmed/22456780>.

Mosby's Medical Dictionary. 8th Edition. St. Louis: Mosby Elsevier, 2009. Print.

New, Susan A., Simon P. Robins, et al. "Dietary influences on bone mass and bone
    metabolism: further evidence of a positive link between fruit and vegetable consumption and
    bone health?." *American Journal of Clinical Nutrition.* 71.1 (2000): 142-151. Web. 30 Mar.
    2012. <http://www.ajcn.org/content/71/1/142>.

Pham, P., J.M. Miller, et al. "Lower serum magnesium levels are associated with mo
    rapid decline of renal function in patients with diabetes mellitus type 2." *Clinical Nephrology.*
    63.6 (2005): 429-436. Web. <http://cat.inist.fr/?aModele=afficheN&cpsidt=16820118>.

Pollan, Michael. *Food Rules: an Eater's Manual.* First edition. London: Penguin, 2009.
    Print.

Qiang, Z., S. Lee, et al. "Artichoke Extract Lowered Plasma
    Cholesterol and Increased Fecal Bile Acids in Golden Syrian Hamsters." *Phytotherapy
    Research.* (2011): n. page. Web. <http://onlinelibrary.wiley.com/doi/10.1002/ptr.3698/abstract
    ?userIsAuthenticated=false&deniedAccessCustomisedMessage=Page 1 of 3>.

Revee, VE, M Allanson, et al. "Mice Drinking Goji Berry Juice
    (Lycium barbarum) are protected from UV radiation-induced skin damage via antioxidant
    pathways." *Photochem Photobiological Sciences.* 9.4 (2101): 601-607. Web. <http://www.
    ncbi.nlm.nih.gov/pubmed/20354657>.

Schwartz, Joe, Fran Berkoff, et al. *Foods that Harm Foods that Heal.* 2010 ed.
    New York: Metro Books, 2004. Print.

Shah, Meena. "Effect of a High-Fiber Diet Compared With a Moderate-Fiber Diet on Calcium and Other Mineral Balances in Subjects With Type 2 Diabetes." *Diabetes Care*. 32.6 (2009): 990-995. Web. <http://care.diabetesjournals.org/content/32/6/990.short>.

Sherwood, Lauralee. *Fundamentals of Human Physiology*. Fourth Edition. Belmont: Brooks/Cole, 2006. 722. eBook. <http://www.amazon.com/dp/0840062257/ref=rdr_ext_tmb>.

Sigelman, Carol K., and Elizabeth A. Rider. *Life-Span Human Development*. 7th Edition. Belmont: Wadsworth. Cengage Learning, 2009. 88. eBook. <http://www.amazon.com/Life-Span-Human-Development-Carol-Sigelman/dp/1111342733/ref=dp_ob_title_bk>.

Taussig, S.J., and S. Batkin. "Bromelain, the enzyme complex of pineapple (Ananas comosus) and its clinical application. An update." *Journal of Ethnopharmacol* . 22.2 (1988): 191-203. Web. <http://www.ncbi.nlm.nih.gov/pubmed/3287010>.

Tovar, J, A Nilsson, et al. "A diet based on multiple functional concepts improves cardiometabolic risk parameters in healthy subjects.." *Nutrition & Metabolism*. 2.1 (2012): 29. Web. 10 Apr. 2012. <http://www.ncbi.nlm.nih.gov/pubmed/22472183>.

Ukil, A., S. Maity, et al. "Curcumin, the major component of food flavour turmeric, reduces mucosal injury in trinitrobenzene sulphonic acid-induced colitis." *British Journal of Pharmacology*. 39.2 (2003): 209-218. Web. <http://onlinelibrary.wiley.com/doi/10.1038/sj.bjp.0705241/full>.

United States. Centers for Disease Control and Prevention. *2007 National Diabetes Fact Sheet*. Atlanta: 2007. Web. http://www.cdc.gov/diabetes/pubs/figuretext07.html.

United States. Department of Agriculture. *DIETARY REFERENCE INTAKES FOR Vitamin A, Vitamin K, Arsenic, Boron, Chromium, Copper, Iodine, Iron, Manganese, Molybdenum, Nickel, Silicon, Vanadium, and Zinc*. Washington: National Academy Press, 2001. Web. <http://www.nal.usda.gov/fnic/DRI//DRI_Vitamin_A/vitamin_a_full_report.pdf>.

United States. Department of Health and Human Services. *Omega-3 Fatty Acids, Effects on Cardiovascular Risk Factors.* Rockville: Agency for Healthcare Research and Quality, 2004. Web. <http://www.ahrq.gov/clinic/tp/o3cardrisktp.htm>.

United States. National Cancer Institute. *Tea and Cancer Prevention Fact Sheet .* Washington: US Department of Health and Human Services, 2010. Web. <http://www.cancer. gov/cancertopics/factsheet/prevention/tea>.

"Vitamin A (Retinol)." *University of Maryland Medical Center.* University of Maryland Medical Center, n.d. Web. <http://www.umm.edu/altmed/articles/vitamin-a-000331.htm>.

Weber, Peter. "Vitamin K and bone health." *Nutrition.* 17.10 (2001): 880-887. Web. <http://linkinghub.elsevier.com/retrieve/pii/S0899900701007092>.

Williamson, A M, and Anne-Marie Feyer. "Moderate sleep deprivation produces impairments in cognitive and motor performance equivalent to legally prescribed levels of alcohol intoxication." *Occupational and Environmental Medicine.* 57. (2000): 649-655. Web. 3 May. 2012. <http://oem.bmj.com/content/57/10/649.long>.

Wolever, TM, AL Gibbs, et al. "Bioactive oat ⊠-glucan reduces LDL cholesterol in Caucasians and non-Caucasians.." *Nutrition Journal.* 10.130 (2011). Web.

Wolfe, David. *Eating for Beauty.* Third Edition. San Diego: Sunfood Publishing, 2007. Print.

Wolfe, David. Superfoods: *The Food and Medicine of the Future.* First Edition. Berkely: North Atlantic Books, 2009. Print.

Yang, Chih-Min, I-Hsuan Lu, et al. "Lycopene inhibits the proliferation of androgen-dependent human prostate tumor cells through activation of PPARÎ3-LXRÎ±- ABCA1 pathway ." *Journal of Nutritional Biochemistry* . 23.1 (2012): 8-17. Web. <http://www.jnutbio.com/article/S095 2863(10)00259-7/abstract>.

Yeager, Selene. *The Doctors Book of Food Remedies.* First Edition. New York: Rodale, 2007. Print.

Young, M.M., M.B. Durh, et al. "Effects Of Natural And Artificial Menopause On Plasma And Urinary Calcium And Phosphorus." *Lancet.* 290.7507 (1967): 118-120. Web. <http://www.thelancet.com/journals/lancet/article/PIIS0140-6736(67)92961- 3/abstract>.